The Ashes of Loda

BOOKS BY ANDREW GARVE

Hide and Go Seek
The Ashes of Loda
Frame-up
The Sea Monks
Prisoner's Friend
The House of Soldiers
The Far Sands
The Golden Deed
A Hero for Leanda
The Galloway Case
The Narrow Search
The Megstone Plot
The End of the Track
The Riddle of Samson
Death and the Sky Above
The Cuckoo Line Affair
By-line for Murder
A Hole in the Ground
Murder through the Looking Glass
No Tears for Hilda
Fontego's Folly

The Ashes of Loda

by Andrew Garve

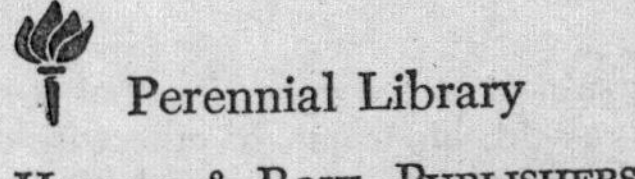

Perennial Library
HARPER & ROW, PUBLISHERS
New York

THE ASHES OF LODA was originally published by Harper & Row, Publishers, Incorporated, in 1965.

First Perennial Library edition published 1966 by Harper & Row, Publishers, Incorporated, New York.

Library of Congress catalog card number: 64:25132

The Ashes of Loda

I

Miss Phelps spoke in the telephone. "Lord Quainton's here now, Mr. Cole. . . . Yes, all right." She gave me a friendly nod. "His Nibs is free—you can go in." I thanked her, and went through into the editor's room.

John Cole got up from his chair and greeted me warmly. "Good to see you back, Tim," he said. He was a tall, lean man with a craggy face. I had worked for him for nearly ten years, first as reporter and then as foreign correspondent. I respected and liked him.

"Pull up a chair," he said. "Sorry I was busy all day yesterday." He settled himself behind his desk, his long legs tied into a comfortable knot. "Well, how are you?"

"I'm fine," I said.

"Health all right? No neuroses? No Moscow blues?"

"Nothing like that."

"Good. You're certainly looking very chipper. . . . So you think you'll be able to stand another spell out there?"

"Oh, yes," I said. "It's an interesting time just now—what with the Chinese quarrel, the harvest failures, and the so-called thaw. Never a dull moment."

"You still don't believe in the thaw?"

"I don't think anyone's going to fall through the ice just yet."

He smiled. "Well, we must have a long talk about all that before you go back. . . . Anyway, Tim, you've been doing an excellent job out there. Sound, objective news coverage, and the sort of thoughtful interpretation that a quality Sunday paper needs."

I acknowledged the compliment and tried not to look too complacent.

"Of course," he went on, after a pause, "keeping a staff man in Moscow is a a bit of a luxury for a weekly paper. You're a big name now and I feel we ought to exploit you more. How would you feel about leaving the routine stuff to the agencies for a while and concentrating on a really ambitious feature?"

"It sounds attractive," I said. "What exactly are you thinking of?"

"Well, I was talking the other day to a man named George Sutton—a timber importer—and he said the Russians had never learned to cope with their winter—economically, industrially—the way the Middle West or Canada has. He said they virtually hibernated, and that this was the thing above all others that was holding them back. Would you agree?"

"I wouldn't put it quite as strongly as that," I said. "But there's a lot in it. . . . They do tend to think of their winter as something to be endured rather than mastered. Not the men at the top, but the masses. The peasants are pretty satisfied if they can just keep alive."

"Which means that everything slows down."

"Oh, tremendously. And the people do seem fairly resigned about it. They're slow and backward by nature, and the climate encourages them in their ways."

Cole nodded. "As I thought, it's an interesting angle. Now you'll be going back there in six weeks' time, at the start of their winter. How about making a winter journey—say, through the Ukraine? A comprehensive trip, covering the collective farms and the Don basin industries. Find out what their winter techniques are like and, if they lag, where they lag. Nothing unfriendly—just a straight inquiry. Then do a long piece—perhaps ten thousand words—with plenty of color and description. You could take your time over it—you could come back here to write it if you liked. We'd run it for several weeks. . . . How does the idea appeal to you?"

"Very much indeed," I said. "There's nothing I'd like better. You know the difficulty, though."

"Getting permission, I suppose."

I nodded. "The thaw definitely hasn't spread to that kind of trip. They wouldn't let me just go off on my own."

"Not even though you speak Russian like a native?"

"That's what would worry them most—I could talk to people too easily. . . . No, they'd want to vet the itinerary and they'd insist on sending someone along with me."

"Would that matter?"

"It wouldn't matter a bit from the story point of view —it might even help. . . . But they take such a long while to organize anything."

"You mean it might be high summer before they were ready?"

"It might easily be *next* winter. Anyway, I'll put it up to the Press Department as soon as I get back, and see what they say."

"Yes, do that—tell them we're very keen on the trip. In the meantime, you can be thinking it over—doing a bit of planning, perhaps." Cole glanced at his watch, unwound his legs and got up. "By the way, I've got Bressov coming to dine tonight—the Counselor at the Embassy. It would be nice if you could join us. Eight o'clock at my home? I apologize for the short notice."

I hesitated—but only for a second. "I'm sorry," I said, "I'm afraid I'm already fixed up for tonight."

"Blast! Is it an important date, Tim? Couldn't you break it?"

I shook my head regretfully. "I really am sorry—I'd have liked to join you."

Cole grimaced. "Well, you're on leave, so I can't make it a command performance. We must lunch together soon —I'll ask Miss Phelps to arrange it with you. . . . And I hope you have an enjoyable holiday."

"Thank you," I said. "I think I'm going to."

At eight o'clock that evening, with only the faintest pricking of conscience, I was sitting at a secluded table in the Gourmet Restaurant in Soho, waiting for a girl I'd met at a cocktail party the night before.

It had been pure chance that I'd gone to it. I'd flown in from Moscow around noon, checked in at a hotel off the Strand, and made a few phone calls to scattered relations. Then I'd wandered along to the office to report to Dukes, the Foreign Editor, and say hullo to old friends. I'd spent a most agreeable afternoon, gossiping and reminiscing, but at short notice no one had been free for the evening and for lack of anything better to do I'd drifted along to a film show and press party to which the paper had received an invitation. The film, a thriller, was supposed to have a Russian background and I was interested to see what the moguls had made of it. The thriller part wasn't bad, but the background was such a travesty of the real thing that I found it hard to sit through the film. The party afterward was like a million others, and I'd just decided to make an early night of it when I noticed a rather unusual-looking girl standing alone. My glance, when she intercepted it, brought a coolly inquiring response. I moved over, glass in hand, with an amiable, cocktail-party smile. She returned the smile. Her face had been rather grave in repose, but her smile was devastating. It ran me through like a sword.

We went into the usual routine, introducing ourselves, and making light conversation at first. She was, it appeared, the personal secretary of the producer, Anton Darlan. She looked about twenty-four. Her English was as accentless as mine, but the name she gave sounded like Maria Rashinsky. I asked her if she was Russian. After a few drinks, and in the context of the evening, it didn't seem too idiotic a question. "No, I'm British," she replied, with a touch of indignation. "Of course," I said, "stupid of me!" We both laughed. It turned out that she spelled her name Raczinski—and Marya with a "y." Her father had been a Pole but he'd long ago become naturalized and she'd been brought up wholly in England. She'd dropped the feminine form "Raczinska," she said, to avoid confusion.

I was fascinated by her. She was a tall brunette with greenish eyes and an air of tremendous distinction. She was beautifully groomed, she had poise, she appeared very sophisticated—yet once we'd got over the frothy preliminaries, her conversation had a naturalness and directness which I'd previously associated only with Russian girls. And that smile! The old cliché about a face lighting up exactly described what happened. I found myself working for it, longing for it to reappear. It was enchanting—and so was she. She wore no ring, which seemed incredible. We got on so well together that before the party broke up I dared to ask her if she'd dine with me next day—and to my astonished delight she said yes.

So here I was at the Gourmet, a fairly hard-bitten newspaperman with a quickened pulse; a bachelor of thirty crazily toying with the idea of abandoning his freedom if he were given half a chance—all on the strength of a smile and an hour's talk.

I'd been sitting at the table, anxiously watching the door, for more than twenty minutes when she arrived. I saw her come in and speak to the head waiter and I waved as she turned in my direction. There was a slightly puzzled expression on her face as she joined me.

"I'm sorry I'm so late . . ." she began.

"You came," I said, "that's all that matters."

"The traffic's impossible."

"Don't give it a thought. Where I come from, people reckon they're keeping an appointment if they turn up on the right day." I helped her with her coat. "What would you like to drink—gin, sherry. . . ?"

"Tio Pepe, please."

I ordered the sherry, and a Martini for myself, and the waiter went away.

"You know," she said, "I could have sworn the head waiter said *Lord* Quainton when I asked for you."

"I expect he did. I've been here before."

"You mean you *are* a lord?"

"Yes."

"Oh!"

"I hope you don't mind."

"Of course not. . . ." She didn't sound too certain about it.

"I could disclaim the title," I said.

She laughed. "I was surprised, that's all. . . . The only lords I know are bald and elderly."

"Oh, we come all ages."

The drinks arrived. I raised my glass. "Well, it's nice to see you again, Marya. It's been a long time."

"You're rather foolish," she said. She sipped her sherry. "Do you like being a lord?"

"It has some advantages. The obvious social ones, of course. . . . Professionally, it sometimes helps to open doors. Oddly enough, the Russians are rather impressed with titles. . . . And then it's quite a satisfactory thought that if I felt strongly enough about something I could take my seat in the House of Lords and make a fuss."

"Will you ever? Take your seat, I mean?"

"I might—though I'll have to make up my mind fairly soon. . . . I would never have wanted to be an M.P.—my father was one, and from what I saw of the life it was deadly. Mostly he spent his time as a sort of welfare officer for his constituents—overworked and underpaid. In the end he was made a baron because a prospective Minister wanted his seat. That accounts for me—I'm the second baron. No blue blood, you see—just jiggery-pokery."

The waiter was hovering, with enormous menus. "Shall we order," I said, "and then we can talk in peace." Marya chose melon and escalope de veau Marsala, which was a specialty of the house. I said I'd have the same. With Marya opposite me, looking perfectly delectable, I'd have been just as happy with a sandwich. I ordered a bottle of claret, which I thought she'd like, and relaxed.

"You know," I said, "this is quite the most agreeable thing I've done in years."

"Really? Don't you enjoy yourself in Moscow?"

" 'Enjoy' is a strong word. One has one's moments—but it's not exactly a carefree place."

"How did you come to be sent there?"

"Well, it all started with doing a Russian course in an intelligence unit when I was a National Service man. You had to work hard and show results or they sent you back to square-bashing—so naturally I worked hard. Afterwards it seemed a waste not to use the language. I got a job reporting for the *Sunday Recorder* and when a chance came I applied for the Moscow post. I've been there three years now."

"And you only come back once a year?"

"Yes—unless something special arises. . . . It's not a life sentence, of course, just a stretch."

That earned me another smile.

There was a little pause while the waiter served the melon. Then Marya said, "Isn't the end of October rather late to take your holiday? I shouldn't think you'll have very good weather."

"No," I agreed. "I generally go south for a couple of weeks, to France or Italy—though I somehow doubt if I will this time. . . . Anyway, the weather can't be worse here than it is in Russia—the between-seasons are always frightful there. When the snow melts in the spring, every track turns into a quagmire. They call it *rasputitsa*—it means roadlessness. And conditions in the autumn are nearly as bad. Once the snow settles for good, things can be quite pleasant, but it usually falls and melts several times before it stays. To me, autumn in Moscow means long queues of sullen people in wet clothes standing about for hours in icy slush. At least I'll be missing that."

"It sounds frightful. . . . What do they queue for?"

"Oh, practically everything. Food, tickets, passes, permits—there's always a queue. It's the national pastime. . . . There's a rather nice story . . ."

"I'm listening."

"Well, there was a Muscovite named Ivan who badly wanted a train ticket to Leningrad. He knew he hadn't much hope of getting one at the ticket office, because there was always a tremendous queue and hardly any tickets. Then he remembered that he had a friend at the Commissariat of Transport and he went along and explained his need. His friend was sympathetic, and gave him a permit to go to the head of the queue. Ivan was naturally delighted. He took his permit and went boldly to the head of the queue and rapped on the counter. The man who was already first in line said, 'What do you think you're up to, comrade? You get to the back.' Ivan, undismayed, said, 'It's all right, comrade—I have a permit to go to the head of the queue.' The other man looked at him pityingly. 'Comrade,' he said, 'this is the queue for people with permits to go to the head of the queue.' "

We both laughed. Marya said, "I must remember to tell that to my father—he'll love it."

We went on talking about Russia for some time. I hadn't intended to—it's a subject I can easily get carried away by—but Marya because of her Polish connections, I guessed, was more than ordinarily interested. What I really wanted to talk about was herself, and as soon as I got the chance I switched the conversation to her job with the film company. "Do you enjoy it?" I asked her.

"Very much, most of the time. Everyone in the film world is absolutely scatty, of course—but once you accept that, it can be great fun."

"Do you see much of the actual film making?"

"Sometimes I do—it depends on Anton. Last year he made a picture in Spain and I was with him on location for six weeks. It was very hot and everyone got frightfully bad-tempered. . . . My real job is to prevent Anton getting ulcers. He's a sweet man, but hopelessly temperamental—and so incompetent about ordinary day-to-day living it's just not true. I spend most of my time smoothing his path."

"It sounds like a key job to me."

"It is," Marya said seriously. "I often think the company wouldn't last a month without me."

I smiled. Her lack of false modesty was most refreshing. "How long have you been working for them?" I asked.

"Nearly three years."

"What were you doing before that?"

"I was up at Oxford, taking an Arts degree."

"And before that?"

She made a face. "Finishing school in Switzerland."

"And before that?"

"Boarding school at Eastbourne. . . . Now you really *do* sound like a newspaperman."

"Genuine personal interest, I assure you."

"Then I forgive you. . . . But if it's my life story you're after, I can tell you right away it's very dull. I've led a most conventional existence. . . . All the important and dramatic things happened before I was old enough to take them in. Before I was three, actually."

"But you know about them?"

"Yes, of course. . . ."

"Then may I hear?"

"Are you sure you want to? It's a rather grim story."

"As long as it won't spoil your dinner."

"Oh, it won't do that—it's all old history now. . . . Well—I was born in Lvov, in Poland, in the middle of the war. My father had just graduated at the university there when the war started. He'd also just got married. He was very young, only twenty-one, but he'd been left a little money—and he had tremendous confidence in himself. . . . Then Hitler's invasion shattered everything. First the Russians came, and then the Germans, and ordinary life disintegrated. Daddy had to do any job he could, just to get enough to eat. Then, in 1942, the Nazis sent him to a labor camp. They wanted to destroy Poland, and rounding up all the intellectuals and working them to death was one of their ways. Daddy was lucky—he was one of the few to survive. He was in camps for the rest of the war.

The last one was the worst of all—it was called Loda. Have you heard of it?"

"Yes, indeed," I said. "It's notorious. . . . The Russians have turned the site into a museum—'lest we forget' and all that. But I've never been."

"Apparently the most appalling things happened there. Daddy would never talk about the really hair-raising things, but what he did tell me was bad enough. . . . Anyway, when the Red army overran the camp in 1944 he escaped in the confusion and joined some other Poles in the forest. He fought the Nazis as a guerrilla for about three months and then he was shot in the knee. That completely put him out of action, of course. He lay hidden in a farmhouse for weeks afterwards, while he recovered. It was really the end of the war for him."

"And what about you?"

"The only thing I'd done was to get born. That was in 1942, just before Daddy was taken away. Soon afterward, my mother died. People were dying in thousands at that time, of hunger and neglect. There weren't any near relations who could take care of me and I was looked after by some neighbors—an old couple called Komarovski. Daddy learned all this when he made his way back to Lvov after the German collapse. It must have been a ghastly homecoming for him—but at least he found me. Then his one idea was to get to the West, to take me out of it all—and he set off on foot, as thousands of others were doing, carrying me. We finished up in a displaced persons' camp near Cologne. All the DP's wanted to get to England or America, but there were quotas and it wasn't easy. Daddy was one of the fortunate ones—he had qualifications in chemistry, so he had a prospect of earning his living. Anyway, we made it."

"And then what?"

"Oh, that was really the end of our troubles. There were already a lot of Poles here and they had an organization to help newcomers. Because Daddy had a degree he was put in touch with an odd-sounding body called the

Society for the Promotion of Learning and they were terribly good to him. They got him a research grant and a place to work at London University. After a while he was chosen as an assistant by a professor there called Malins. He'd learned English, of course, and as soon as he could he became naturalized and we settled down for good. There was a sort of nanny-housekeeper named Lucy who looked after us. She was a sweetie—I was very fond of her. . . . So I grew up. And that's really all."

"It's a terrific story," I said.

"It is, rather, isn't it? Especially as it had a happy ending."

"Is your father still at the University?"

"No, he left it in 1955—he decided he couldn't manage on an academic salary any more. He took a job with Floria Products—the cosmetic people. He's their chief chemist now."

"It sounds a big change. Does he like it?"

"He says he does—though I've an idea he finds the work very limited after what he was doing. Personally, I think it's a great pity he gave up his academic work, because he's a brilliant man and I'm sure he could have gone a long way in research. But he was absolutely determined to give me the best possible education and background—and that meant a lot of expense. . . . If I'd been old enough I'd have argued with him, but of course I wasn't."

"He's probably found the sacrifice well worthwhile," I said. "I'm sure that watching you grow up as an English young lady must have given him a great deal of pleasure."

"Oh, I think it has."

"One way and another, he sounds a pretty remarkable man."

"He is."

"Do you live with him?"

"Yes, we have a flat in Hampstead. He drives out to the laboratory at Welwyn each morning, and I come into town, and if we're both free in the evening we dine together."

"I'd like to meet him some time."

Marya smiled. "We'll see," she said.

I'd had a wonderful evening, and my one desire at parting was to make another date. In fact there was no difficulty—Marya seemed very willing. She had an engagement for the following night, she said, but on the next day—a Saturday—she'd be free. I suggested that if the weather was reasonable we might drive out into the country and perhaps have a picnic and a walk. She said she'd love that, and I arranged to pick her up at Charing Cross underground station at ten in the morning.

I spent most of Friday looking for a hire car that would do justice to her, and praying that the weather would improve. I was fortunate in both respects. I managed to get hold of a nearly new Mercedes, and the glass rose steadily. Saturday turned out to be an almost perfect late-October day—dry, sunny and mellow. I got the hotel to pack a lunch basket for two, and at ten o'clock I was waiting at Charing Cross for Marya's arrival. She appeared at a quarter past ten, smiling and sweet. She was wearing a tweed skirt, a suède jacket, and sensible shoes. "What a divine day!" she said. "Aren't we lucky?" She admired the car and asked where we were going.

"Is there anywhere you'd specially like to go?"

"Well," she said, "since you ask me, there is. Do you know Chanctonbury Ring?"

"On the South Downs? Yes, I know of it—I've never actually been there."

"Neither have I, but it's one of Daddy's favorite spots. He goes down to Sussex to fish quite often, when he wants to be alone—and if the fish aren't rising, he walks. He says the view from the Ring is marvelous. . . . Do you think it's too far?"

"No," I said, "I think it's about right. . . . Let's go."

We had a most enjoyable run, once we were out of the suburbs. The bright weather had brought out a lot of cars and people, but we weren't in any hurry. The Mercedes was a delight to drive. Marya's scent was a subtle enchantment. As far as I was concerned, the day could go on forever. I concentrated on the driving, and let Marya talk. She was completely relaxed, and obviously happy to be with me. It seemed incredible that, two days before, we hadn't known each other.

We reached the South Downs just before noon. At a place called Storrington, Marya spotted a pub, the "Three Crowns," which apparently was where her father always stayed on his fishing trips, and we went in for a drink and a look round. Then, after checking with the map, we drove on to the little village of Washington and parked the car at the foot of the hill we were going to climb. The Ring was just visible from the road—a circular copse of ancient trees crowning the eight-hundred-foot summit. A chalky path wound steeply up to it through smooth, sheep-cropped turf. We attacked the hill with vigor. At the film party where I'd met Marya I'd have said she was a town girl, but she went up that hill like a Sherpa. In less than twenty minutes we were standing on the top.

The view from the Ring was superb. The ground fell away on all sides, so that we seemed to be on top of the world. Down in the valley there were several parked cars besides our own, and the lower slopes were dotted with people, but up here we were quite alone. To the north, the flat plain of farms and fields stretched away into a golden haze. To the south, it was just possible to make out the pale blue line of the sea. The thyme-scented air was very still. The only sounds we could hear were the twitter of a skylark above us and the bleating of sheep.

Marya's eyes were shining. "No wonder Daddy likes to come here," she said. "Isn't it marvelous, Tim?"

"Wonderful," I said. "Everything's wonderful." She looked up at me, and I kissed her mouth. She kissed me back—shyly at first, then less shyly. I hadn't thought of her as passionate, but she was.

"This could grow on us," she said, suddenly releasing herself. "Perhaps we'd better have lunch."

We sat down and Marya opened the lunch basket. The hotel had done us well. There was cold turkey and salad, crisp French bread and butter, William pears and a flask of coffee. "It's a feast," Marya said, "not a picnic." She spread a cloth on the grass and methodically arranged everything. "Right," she said, "help yourself." We were both hungry after our climb and for the next fifteen minutes we ate more than we talked.

It was after the meal was over and we were lazily stretched out on the turf that Marya said, "Tim, tell me about your family. Is your mother alive?"

"No—she died several years ago."

"Have you any brothers or sisters?"

"Yes—two of each."

"Where do they live?"

"One brother's in Wales, one in Vancouver. I've a sister in Northumberland and another in Devon."

"You Quaintons get about, don't you?"

"Yes, quite a bit."

"Are they married?"

"Three of them are. I've two small nephews and one niece."

"Do you all get on well together?"

"Pretty well. . . . I don't see much of them these days, of course. But we're quite a closely knit family."

She gave a little sigh. "How I envy you!"

"Yes," I said, "I can understand that."

"I've a lot of friends, but it's not the same thing as a family. Daddy's the only blood relation I've ever known—or ever will know. Sometimes it makes me feel—well—very rootless."

"Wasn't your father able to trace any of your relations?"

"There weren't any, to speak of. He was an only child, and so was my mother. And all the old people must have died long ago."

"H'm—you're a real orphan of the storm, aren't you? What about Lucy—the nanny-housekeeper you told me about? Don't you still see her? She must have been quite a mother to you."

"She was—especially when I was young. But four years ago, when I was eighteen, she met an American and married him and went to live in California. I was glad for her sake—but I miss her a lot."

"Do you write to each other?"

"Oh, yes—but it's not the same."

"No . . ." I reached out and took her hand in mind. "Of course, Marya, you know the best thing to do if you feel the lack of a family?"

"What's that?"

"Acquire one," I said.

That day on the Downs was the real start of my courtship of Marya. I'd gone completely overboard for her and I left her in no doubt about my feelings. She was less forthcoming in words, but the fact that she was content to spend most of her free time with me gave me all the encouragement I needed. During the next week or two we were together almost every evening, and often at midday as well. We dined and danced, we went to theaters, we went to the ballet. At week ends we drove out of London to places that one or other of us had liked and remembered. We strolled in woods, we walked along sea walls, we visited stately homes. We had a wonderful time.

From Marya's point of view it must have seemed a bit of a blitzkrieg and in the ordinary way I wouldn't have rushed things quite so much. Getting to know each other was too enjoyable to hurry over. But as it was I seemed to have no choice, because of having to go back to Moscow. I wanted Marya for keeps, not for a season, and I felt that if we didn't reach some sort of understanding before I left, my chance might slip away. She had been, I gathered, practically engaged when she was twenty-one, but it hadn't worked out—which explained why she was still unattached, and was my good fortune. It certainly didn't mean that she'd be available forever. She was, I guessed, by no means a dedicated career girl; and if it was humanly possible I meant to leave a ring on her finger before I went away. At this stage neither of us specifically mentioned marriage, but of course it was in both our minds.

We talked endlessly about ourselves and each other as my leave burned up—trying to compress what would normally have been the exploration of months into a few weeks. The more I learned of Marya, the more deeply I fell in love with her. I think what appealed to me most about her—apart from her physical attraction and the warm promise it held—was the honesty and genuineness of her personal feelings. It was, I decided, a particularly Slav trait, for I'd noticed it in many Russians as well—the lack of coquetry, the directness of response, the composed silence when there was nothing to say, the bubbling liveliness when the talk grew interesting. Marya had a loyalty to her true self, a total absence of pretense, which no veneer of upbringing or education could hide. It seemed to me a rare and precious quality.

We were often very gay in those halcyon weeks—but we had our earnest moments, too, discussing Life and Death and the World and the Bomb as though they were all virgin topics. Marya was essentially a serious-minded person, with a point of view of her own about most things—usually a hopeful, confident point of view. I couldn't always share her optimistic outlook, but I infinitely preferred her proud, up-beat, positive attitude to life to the current nihilism. She had a sense of continuity and history, a serenity about the future which was very impressive. In fact, she was impressive altogether—a strong and vital personality. If it hadn't been for that smile of hers, I might have had doubts whether I'd be able to cope. As it was, I thought we'd be pretty well matched.

Very often, in our talks, she mentioned her father. She had an enormous regard for him, and they were obviously very close—though not, as I'd already discovered with some relief, inseparable. He'd always been deeply absorbed in his work, Marya said, and he'd encouraged her to be independent and self-reliant, to make her own friends, to take her own holidays. It seemed a very sound and normal relationship. What Marya hadn't mentioned before, but told me now, was that she was rather concerned about his health. He was, it appeared, a worrier, and he'd had a succession of minor anxiety illnesses that had left him very depressed—without any reason that anyone had been able to discover. Probably, she thought, his experiences during the war years had taken more of a toll of him than he'd realized, and the strain was now beginning to show.

"It's a pity he never remarried," she said. "It might have taken his mind off himself. At one time I thought he might ask Lucy to marry him—he seemed very fond of her, and she was devoted to him. I'm sure she'd have said yes, and I think it would have worked out well for both of them. . . . I suggested it once—but Daddy just shook his head rather sadly and said he didn't think he wanted to marry a second time. It was soon after that that Lucy left us. . . . I suppose he'd never really got over the tragedy in Poland. Poor Daddy!"

It seemed an opportune moment for me to say again that I'd very much like to meet her father. This time Marya didn't put me off. She said she'd like me to, and that she'd arrange it.

I went to lunch with the Raczinskis on the following Saturday—not without a certain trepidation when the time came, for I was very anxious to make a good impression on Raczinski *père.* Marya opened the door to me, with a welcoming smile. We kissed briefly, conspiratorially, in the hall. The air was strongly perfumed. "It's not me," Marya said, as I sniffed. "It's Daddy. . . . However hard he tries not to, he always comes home from the lab smelling like a boudoir. I hope you don't mind." I assured her that boudoir was my favorite scent—which got me another smile, slightly reproachful.

"Daddy's just clearing up in the study," she said. "He

won't be long." She took me into the sitting room. The flat was on the top floor of a solidly built Victorian house that itself stood on the top of a hill, and there was a tremendous view westward over roofs and railway lines and trees to what looked almost like open country. Raczinski obviously had a passion for high places. The inside of the flat was pleasantly furnished, though in quite a modest way. There seemed to be books everywhere. As Marya started to pour drinks, my roving eye was caught by a tiny, very faded photograph in a metal frame—of a pretty woman, hardly older than Marya now was. "It's a bit pathetic, isn't it?" Marya said as I studied it. "It was the only photograph of my mother that Daddy was able to salvage. But at least I know what she looked like."

There was a footfall in the hall, and Stefan Raczinski came in. Marya introduced us. Raczinski gave me a formal little bow with his heels together, and we shook hands. "Delighted," he said. He was a man of medium height, very squarely built, with a large head and an imposingly high forehead. He had fine, silvery hair which he wore loose, without a parting. His eyes were green like Marya's, but more deeply set, with dark pouches under them. His face was very lined, and he seemed much older than his forty-six years. As Marya had said, he looked like a man who had taken a beating from life and was under very heavy strain.

Marya gave me a Martini and took one herself and we all sat down. Raczinski drank only tonic water—on account of his digestion, he said ruefully. His manner was friendly, if a trifle wary. I could sense him studying and appraising me. We exchanged the usual small talk, feeling our way. His English was fluent and accurate. Like his fellow countryman, Conrad—some of whose works I had noticed on the shelves—he had acquired a fine command of words in his adopted language. But his accent was so strong that at first I had some difficulty in following him. He apologized for it. "I have a good eye for language," he said, "but unfortunately I have no ear. I am just comprehensible in English, impossible in French. As for German, I have never succeeded in getting my tongue round their words. Not," he added, "that I wish to." He eyed me sardonically. "So you are a correspondent in Moscow, Lord Quainton. Now what have you done to deserve that fate?"

I laughed. "It's not really as bad as all that."

"You like the Russians?" He had the same directness of manner as Marya. In his case I found it slightly disconcerting.

"I don't like their political setup," I said. "But as people, I like them very much."

He grunted. "What would you say their more admirable qualities are—as people?"

I sipped my Martini and searched for appropriate words. "Sincerity in relationships," I said. "Respect for other people's feelings. Loyal friendship if they take to you."

He savored the phrases. "H'm. . . . Well, you may be right. . . . You have seen them, of course, only at peace—not as invaders."

"That's true."

Marya, with a smile, said, "Now don't start getting worked up, Daddy—you know it's not good for you." But he took no notice. He was obviously determined to make his own attitude clear.

"As a former Pole," he said, "I can forgive neither the Russians nor the Germans. The Nazis, of course, were unspeakable—their name will be a curse forever. They were barbarians and they laid waste our country. But the Russians, in their callous way, were hardly better—and we had them on our necks for much longer. Their imperialism goes back for generations. My great-grandfather was executed for plotting against them. And in the last war, they were guilty of fearful crimes. At Katyn Forest, Stalin had ten thousand Polish Officers murdered—the flower of our army. In cold blood. But then he had no warm blood. He was a monster."

"He's been dead a long while," Marya said. "And times have changed."

Raczinski shook his head doubtfully. "I would like to think so. . . . But the Russians still tyrannize over much of eastern Europe. They still hold the territories that they stole after the war. Our own birthplace—Lvov—is now a part of Russia." He pronounced it "Lvooff," in the Polish way. "You who are born English, Lord Quainton, do not always appreciate how fortunate you are. To have escaped conquest for centuries, to live without fear in a free society—that is really to be blessed. Freedom is the most precious of all possessions. Poland has rarely known it. . . ." He smiled wryly. "But there, I will not bore you any longer with my old hatreds. After all, I am now English, too, so I must be tolerant. . . . I would have liked, though, to see Lvov again, just once, before I died."

"Is there no chance of that?" I asked him. "Not even as a tourist?"

"Not for me. . . . From the Russian point of view, I committed the unforgivable sin after I escaped from the camp at Loda. Marya will have told you about Loda. . . . I could have gone to the East and joined the Russians—as some did. Instead, I chose to come to the West. In their eyes, that was the choice of an enemy. . . . In any case, I am not sure that I would really wish to see Lvov under established Communist rule. It is better that I should try to remember it as the happy place it was before the war."

"Is it an attractive town?"

"It is not breathtakingly beautiful, like Cracow, but it is very pleasant. Even after the damage of war, it remained pleasant. It lies in a broad valley with a pretty river running through it—the Peltew, where I learned to fish. And it is close to the mountains. My boyhood, as I remember it, was spent almost entirely in the open air. We lived in a house in Biesczady Street—a white, three-storied house with big, sunny balconies—and immediately opposite there was a lovely park—not formal, except for one fountain, but wild and hilly—a place for children to play in. I had only to slip across the road to be in paradise. . . ." He gave a little sigh. "I tell myself often that I must not live in the past—especially as I have been so fortunate in England. I have found such kindness and friendship that to dwell on what is gone would be ungrateful. . . . But the Poles, I am afraid, are incorrigibly romantic." His eyes suddenly twinkled. "About their country, their horses—and their women."

"Well—thanks!" Marya said.

Raczinski got up, went to a cupboard, and unromantically popped a pill into his mouth. I noticed that he limped a little—and Marya saw that I noticed.

"Daddy's leg still troubles him a bit sometimes."

I made sympathetic noises.

"It is nothing," Raczinski said. "Again, I was very fortunate. If the bullet had struck a fraction higher, my knee would have been smashed—and that would probably have been the end of me. . . . Instead, it cut through behind the knee." He demonstrated, clutching the back of his trouser leg. "Not even a tendon was severed. It becomes a little stiff only when I take no exercise. That is why I like to climb high hills—and high staircases. After I have exercised for a while, I feel nothing. . . . Now, Lord Quainton, let me refill your glass. . . ."

I'd begun to wonder how well I was going to get on with Marya's father. I could see that he was a redoubtable figure, a man of forceful personality—and that was fine. But he seemed a bit too opinionated and egocentric for my taste. Also, I'd found his nostalgia for his boyhood embarrassingly sentimental. Then, over a most agreeable lunch, I changed my mind about him. He, too, I concluded, had been nervous about our meeting. As we grew more used to each other he stopped talking about himself, and the conversation lost its harsh political edge. He proved to be an attentive host and, surprisingly, an urbane listener. There was evidently a lot more to him than met the ear. When, after lunch, Marya and I went for a walk across Hampstead Heath in the pale November sun, and she asked me if I liked her father, I was able to say quite honestly that I did.

She looked very relieved. "It's odd—I've never heard him talk quite so bitterly about the past as he did today. But then he has been rather upset lately—and he did have a terrible time. In his place, I'm sure I'd feel just as strongly. . . . Anyway, you liked him—that's what matters. . . . He liked you, too—very much."

"I'm glad of that," I said. With the parental hurdle taken, the moment seemed ripe to talk about the future. "Marya—when are we going to get married?"

Her hand tightened on mine. For a second or two she said nothing. Then she looked up at me, searching my face. "Are you quite sure you want to?"

"You know I want to. More than anything in the world. I love you, Marya. I'll always love you. . . ."

"I want to marry you, Tim. . . . I'm just a little—afraid, that's all."

"Of what, for goodness' sake?"

"Oh, I don't know. . . . Of being Lady Quainton, perhaps. Of your solid background. Of your family . . ."

"Nonsense—they'll adore you. If we weren't so pushed for time we'd make a tour of them, and then you'd see."

"There seems so much to live up to. And I feel I've so little to give you. An orphan of the storm. . . !"

It was honest misgiving, not false humility. I knew that. Even so, I became a little impatient.

"Listen," I said, "let's get this straight once and for all. I'm an ordinary person—you've absolutely nothing to live up to. And you've everything to give me. You're lovely, you're honest, you're loyal, you're clever—what else could anyone want? A castle in Poland and a bunch of retainers. . . ? Darling, marrying you is the greatest privilege I could ask. I'll be the luckiest, proudest man in the world -and probably the most possessive. . . . Now will you please stop talking rubbish?"

She smiled. "All right," she said. "We'll get married."

I held her close and we kissed.

"When?" I asked.

"If only it could be today!"

I put in the highest bid I could. "I've still got a week. We could marry, and you could come back with me to Moscow."

"Oh, darling, that would be wonderful. . . . But I don't think I can. I must give Daddy time to get used to the idea—I don't want him to feel suddenly abandoned. And I couldn't leave Anton without any warning at all. . . . Couldn't you fly back—say at Easter?"

"Five months?"

"I know—it seems ages. But we could write often—and we'd have so much to look forward to. The time would soon go."

"I suppose so. . . ." I could see her point about her father and Anton. "All right," I said, "that's settled, then. Easter it is. . . ." I drew her to me again. "Darling Marya—it's so good to be alive."

With my leave running out, the problem now was to find time for all the things we had to do. Marya wanted us to have a little celebration with her father and receive his blessing, which we did. Then there were one or two friends she was anxious I should meet before I left—notably a girl named Tina Howell, whom she'd known from college days and often went on holiday with, and who worked on BBC Children's Hour. We went down to Richmond to see Tina one evening and she was a plump blonde, rather plain but very lively and gay, and I got on fine with her. In return I insisted on showing off Marya to one or two friends of mine, which took up some drinking time. There was also the ring to get. On the Wednesday, I arranged with Marya that we would meet for a quick lunch and then go together to choose it. That left me with some free time in the morning and I decided to spend it in the office library, working on my projected Ukraine trip with the help of a map.

In the corridor outside the Foreign Room I ran into the Diplomatic Correspondent, James Gardner, a lean and stooping man of fifty. The veteran of a hundred fruitless international conferences and innumerable diplomatic crises, James usually wore an air of extreme worldly pessimism—and today was no exception.

"You're looking very smug, Tim," he said. "Is it possible that you see a ray of hope?"

I laughed. "As a matter of fact, I've just fixed up to get married."

"Dear boy, I've been married for twenty-five years. . . . *I* don't look smug."

"You can keep your cynicism," I said. "I'm on top of the world."

"Well, I'm glad. . . . Who's the lucky girl?"

"Her name's Marya Raczinski."

"Please God, not a Russian!"

"No, you fascist beast. She was born a Pole, though you wouldn't know it now. Her father came over after the war—Stefan Raczinski. . . ."

"Stefan Raczinski . . ." James frowned. "Now that name rings a faint bell."

"Oh? It didn't with me."

"You're probably too young. I'm almost sure I remember a Stefan Raczinski in the news. . . . Some case—years ago . . . It could have been a different man, of course."

"I expect so."

"Anyway, congratulations. . . . When are you going back to the Red Mecca?"

I grinned. "You'd better not let the Chinese hear you calling it that. . . . Actually, in three days' time."

"Sooner you than me," James said. "I'd rather be buried alive in a lead coffin than work in that place. . . . Tell me, what do *you* think of the thaw?"

We chatted longer than I'd meant to, and when I eventually reached the library there wasn't a lot of time left before lunch. Still, I'd be able to sketch out a rough itinerary and make a few notes. I took down an atlas and opened it at a map of the Ukraine. Where was it Cole had suggested I should go to—the Don basin? Yes, that made sense—a big industrial complex. I might look in at Odessa, too—a port would have problems of its own. And Kiev, the capital. I'd have to try to work out a round trip. . . . I picked up a pencil and sat for a moment idly twirling it, looking at the map but not really concentrating. Something was nagging at me. That remark of James' about Raczinski. There couldn't be many men of that name in England. Perhaps after all his Raczinski *was* the same as mine. In that case I wouldn't mind knowing what the incident was that he'd half remembered. I got up and went over to the personal files. They were very comprehensive and went back for years. I found the "R" shelf and fingered through the folders. Sure enough, there was one marked "RACZINSKI, Stefan, Dr." It was so slim that at first I thought it must be empty, but when I opened it I found just one yellowish clipping inside.

It was from the *Post,* quoting an agency message from Moscow. The date was June 11th, 1953. The message said:

> The Moscow evening newspaper *Vechernaya Moskva* today carried a report that a Dr. Stefan Raczinski has been condemned in absentia by a special court to ten years' imprisonment for war crimes allegedly committed in Loda camp in 1944. According to Soviet sources, Dr. Raczinski is at present resident in England and is working at the University of London.

Above the text was a photograph of Marya's father.

It was a horrible shock. I stared at the paragraph, unable for a moment to think coherently; aware only of an onslaught of impressions, all of them ugly. *War crimes. . . .* The beastliest of all crimes, committed in an atmosphere of beastliness. Kaleidoscopic pictures flashed through my mind—of SS sadists, perverted scientists, monsters in hiding. . . . The thought that Marya's father could have been mixed up with such things was appalling—and I loathed the feeling of being in any way associated with them myself.

That was my first reaction—emotional recoil. Then I took a grip on myself. I began to consider the charge more coolly, in the light of my own knowledge. And I didn't think it could be true. Not of Raczinski. Not of Marya's father. Our acquaintance had been short, but I felt I knew him well enough not to believe a thing like that of him. There must be some simple explanation. A mistake had been made. Someone had blundered. . . . Or lied. . . . The source of the charge could hardly be more tainted. A Moscow newspaper. How much truth came out of Moscow. . . ?

Thus I reassured myself. . . . But the charge had been made—and I knew about it. I'd read the damned paragraph; and I didn't think I could ignore it. I wondered if Marya knew. Suddenly all the joy had gone out of the day. If, as I thought most likely, she didn't know, how would she take it?

I wondered why Raczinski hadn't spoken about it. I couldn't help feeling that he'd been less than frank with me. Here, surely, was the overriding reason why he would never be able to return to Lvov. . . .

I read the clipping through again. I sat thinking about it for quite a while. Finally I slipped it into my pocket-book and went off, troubled and uncertain, to meet Marya.

She was already seated at the luncheon counter, with a plate of food before her. I hadn't realized until then how late I was. She was looking very attractive—and only slightly reproachful.

"I presume you had a busy morning," she said, with a smile. She moved her handbag from the stool she'd been keeping for me and I slid in beside her.

"I'm terribly sorry," I said. "I ran into an old friend—James Gardner—and we got talking. I'll gobble to catch up. What are you eating?"

"What does it look like, sweetie? Cold ham and salad. . . . You seem a bit distrait."

"Do I?"

"Yes, you do. Is something the matter?"

"Not really. . . ."

"Oh, come on—tell."

I took a deep breath. If I was going to mention the thing at all, I might just as well get it over. "Well," I said, "I was telling James about us. He knew your name, Raczinski—said it rang a bell, but he couldn't remember why. So I looked in the office files—and I found a damn stupid newspaper clipping."

"A clipping? What about?"

"About your father. . . . But perhaps you know?" I fished out the slip of paper and passed it to her.

She read it through, slowly.

"It's ten years old," I said, in case she hadn't noticed the date.

Anger and incredulity showed in her face. "But this is monstrous!"

"You didn't know?"

She shook her head. "Daddy never said anything to me about it. . . . How *dare* they?"

"Well, I wouldn't lose any sleep over it."

She looked hard at me. "I hope *you* won't."

"Not me," I said lightly—perhaps too lightly.

"It seems to have been very much on your mind."

"Well, it shook me a bit at first, of course—just as it has you. But it's not a thing to take seriously—the Russians are always making wild charges against people. I should know."

"It's horrible. . . ." She was silent for a moment. "Tim—we must talk to Daddy about it. This evening. . . ."

I shrugged. "If you want to, of course we will."

"I do want to." She slid off her stool. "I think, if you

don't mind, I'll be getting back to the office now. Perhaps you'd collect me at six?"

"But the ring, darling. . . ."

"I'm not in the mood today, Tim. I'm sorry. We'll go another day."

She picked up her bag, gave me a curt little nod, and marched out. It had been even worse than I'd feared.

I called for Marya sharp at six and we drove to Hampstead in a heavy commuter stream. Marya was preoccupied and silent in the car and I fell in with her mood and concentrated on survival in the traffic.

Raczinski wasn't home when we arrived at the flat but he came in shortly afterward. He shook hands with me, as he always did when we met, and Marya kissed him affectionately and asked him if he'd had a good day and poured him a tonic water, and some drinks for us. Then she said, "By the way, Daddy, Tim came across this little item in his office library today," and gave him the clipping.

Raczinski read it through slowly—then turned to me with a rather rueful smile. "I see one should never choose a newspaperman as a prospective son-in-law. I had almost forgotten this incident. . . ." He continued to smile. "Do I have to deny the charge?"

"Of course not," I said. "It was Marya who wanted to talk to you about it. . . ." I grinned feebly. "Though I won't pretend I'm not curious."

Marya said, "Why did you never tell me, Daddy?"

"Well, my dear, you were only about twelve at the time, and you were away at boarding school. There was absolutely no point in worrying you with a thing like this unless someone else mentioned it—and evidently no one did. There was very little in the papers about it."

"I noticed there was only one clipping," I said. "I'm surprised—I'd have thought someone would have tried to interview you."

"Oh, one or two reporters did come to see me—but I had nothing to say. I was not an important person, and anyhow

I dislike publicity. . . . As for telling you later, Marya, it didn't occur to me. The charge was nonsense, and it soon went out of my mind."

"Yes, I see," Marya said.

"Didn't you try to find out a bit more about it at the time?" I asked.

"I can't say I made any great effort, Tim. I did ask the Foreign Office if they knew anything, but they were almost as much in the dark as I was. Apparently the report appeared only in this one Moscow newspaper, and it was very vague. There were two witnesses, neither of whom meant anything to me. They said I had betrayed some escape plans to the Loda camp authorities and brought about the death of fifteen men."

"How utterly fantastic!" Marya exclaimed.

"But surely," I said, "the F.O. asked the Russians for more information?"

"Yes, and the Russians said they would provide it—but they never did."

"I see. . . . What did the F.O. think was behind it—propaganda?"

Raczinski nodded. "They thought it was just another move in the cold war. The West had often accused the Russians of harboring war criminals—and with good reason, for they were using former SS men in various capacities at that time. The charge against me was regarded as part of their riposte. I was not the first case, by any means—several times before that they had picked on some refugee, usually one who was doing quite well in the country that had given him asylum, and accused him of war crimes. There had even been some death sentences. . . . Anyhow, that was what the Foreign Office thought. Their explanation was a reasonable one—though I am not absolutely sure it was the right one."

"Why—what do *you* think was the motive?"

Raczinski shrugged. "It could have been a mistake. The Russians could have mixed me up with someone else."

"You mean that someone in the camp may have done the

things the witnesses said, and they got the name wrong?"

"It is possible."

"And, having discovered there was a Stefan Raczinski in London who had been at Loda, the Russians pinned it on you."

"Exactly. . . . Some of the facts undoubtedly point to a mistake. You see, at first they made some propaganda about me, over Moscow Radio. Then, suddenly, there was nothing more at all. They had been asked for a description of the man they had condemned—but instead of supplying it they dropped the whole thing. They may have realized their mistake. Naturally, they wouldn't have admitted it. . . . However, this is all guesswork. The Russians are quite incalculable, as you know."

"True," I said, and paused. "I'm a bit surprised the F.O. didn't send out a photograph of you and demand proper identification."

Marya was beginning to look restive. "Daddy's already said he wasn't important, Tim."

"I know, but it's not a very nice thing to happen to any man—even an unimportant one. I'd have thought they'd have followed it up a bit more vigorously."

Raczinski shrugged again. "I did not press them—I had no desire to defend myself against any Russian charge. I was not in the least troubled—and neither were the authorities. They were satisfied the charge was untrue, and that was all that mattered. . . . Now I suggest we forget all about it, and have another drink. . . ."

Raczinski had a dinner appointment that evening, and very soon he left us. The moment the door had closed behind him, Marya said, "Well—are you satisfied?"

"About what?" I asked.

"That Daddy didn't do it?"

"Don't be silly," I said. "Of course I am."

"You seemed very interested in all the details."

"I'm interested in everything the Russians do. . . . Anyway, I can't help asking questions. It's my job."

Her face was strained. "The trouble is, you don't know Daddy as I do. *I* know he *couldn't* have done a thing like that."

"Look, darling," I said, "you're pushing at an open door. It's obvious he didn't."

"Why?"

"Well, I was thinking about it after I left you today. . . . A man who'd done what he was accused of would hardly have crossed Europe in the same name—he'd have changed it. And he wouldn't have told everyone he'd been in Loda camp, either—he'd have kept quiet about it."

Marya grew more distant. "I'm glad you were able to think up arguments to convince yourself."

"Well, what's wrong with that?"

"If you were really satisfied, you wouldn't need to."

"But I've told you I am. I accept everything your father said."

"You accept, yes. But are you *certain?*"

"Yes."

"As certain as that I'm standing here? There isn't the tiniest chink of doubt in your mind?"

I suppose I hesitated. Marya went very pale.

"You're *not* certain," she said. "And you never will be. . . . Oh, *why* did you have to find that horrible clipping. . .?"

I did my utmost to reassure her. I tried everything. But I just couldn't reach her. She'd got this fixed idea about me in her mind and I couldn't shift it, either with love or with reason. In the end we parted miserably, with only a vague understanding that we'd meet the next evening. I spent a wretched night, cursing myself for the clumsy way I'd handled things. I'd felt from the start that that newspaper paragraph could be dynamite—yet I'd blundered on without any proper plan. I could see now that I'd been absolutely crazy to produce those well-meant arguments in Raczinski's defense. But the damage was done. . . .

I tried to telephone Marya at the flat in the morning but she must have left early, for there was no reply. I rang her office, and they said she was meeting Anton for some conference. They thought she'd be back in the afternoon, and I said I'd ring again.

I had a lunch appointment with John Cole that day, and for a couple of hours I had to switch my mind from my personal problems to the international situation and my job. Cole said again how keen he was on the Ukraine trip and I told him I'd given it quite a bit of thought, which wasn't strictly true. I covered up with talk about winter food losses and machine deterioration, and mentioned a few of the places I'd thought of going to, and he seemed quite satisfied. He asked me when I was leaving, and said he'd look forward to getting early news from Moscow. He just couldn't wait for me to be on the job again.

I got back to the hotel just after three. There, I found a note from Marya waiting for me. It had been delivered by hand. I tore it open, praying for some change of heart. It said:

Dear Tim,

I hate having to write this to you, but after what has happened I don't see how I can marry you and I think we'd better call it all off. It seems absurd, when we love each other so much, but I'm afraid this shadow would always be between us and for your sake as well as mine I daren't take the risk. It would be different if you could *prove* the truth to yourself, but that's impossible. As it is, I'd never know a moment's peace. I'd always be imagining you watching me, and wondering—wondering if after all you had introduced some undesirable streak into your family. I couldn't bear it.

I've been so happy with you, darling. I looked forward so much to being your wife. I can hardly believe this is the end for us. I'm as wretched about it as I know you will be. But I honestly think it's the best way.

I'm going away for a few days, because there's really

nothing more to say—at least not now. I think it will be easier for us both if I stay away until you've left. I hope you won't feel angry about this. I do love you very much.

Marya

I rang her office—but they'd obviously had their instructions. Marya wasn't feeling well, they said, and she'd taken a few days' leave. If she wasn't at home they didn't know where I'd find her. I rang Tina Howell on the off-chance Marya had arranged to stay with her in Richmond, but Tina said she hadn't. I waited impatiently till a quarter to seven and then rang Dr. Raczinski in Hampstead.

He sounded very upset. "I was about to telephone you," he said. "You have heard from Marya?"

"Yes, I've had a note from her. . . . Where is she?"

"I am afraid I have no idea. We had a long talk last night—and today she left a note for me, too. She said nothing about where she was going. It has been rather a shock."

So that was that.

"I can hardly tell you, Tim, how sorry I am that this has happened. I think Marya is wrong—stubbornly wrong. I think she has manufactured this trouble for herself. I told her so. I argued with her. I said that in your situation, with no evidence to go on, no way of disproving the allegation, I too would have stopped short of certainty. I said that a newspaperman dealt in facts, not faith, and that in my view you had been remarkably trusting. But I could do nothing with her. She is very proud, and very strong-willed. . . . Pride, that is behind it all."

I didn't feel like discussing her. "Anyway," I said, "I don't accept her decision. Will you tell her that? And I shall write to her."

"Yes, please write. . . . Tim, I feel sure that this is not the end—not if you will be patient. Marya loves you and needs you. In time I think she will become more reasonable. She will see that she is making a mountain out of a tiny, tiny molehill. All will fade into memory, as it should do. I will certainly do my best to bring that about, because all this is a great sadness for me."

"Thank you," I said. "Good-bye, Dr. Raczinski."

Forty-eight hours later, I flew to Moscow.

II

Everything about the Russian capital on that December afternoon seemed to match my dismal mood.

The air was lifeless, the cloud-cover leaden. Thin flakes of snow drifted slowly down. The people around the airport building, swathed in their winter clothes, looked shapeless and glum. Out on the tarmac there was the acrid smell of imperfectly refined petrol; in the buffet and the lounge the equally unpleasant one of stale dust and sweat. I had to wait nearly half an hour for a taxi, and when I did get one it was an old boneshaker with a heater that didn't work. In my light autumn overcoat, I sat and froze.

The view along the route into town was as chilling as the temperature. The fallen snow was dirty and drab and had evidently been lying for some time. Not a building showed any trace of charm or quality. The great blocks of flats along the chaussée were mostly new, yet the cement around their balconies was already beginning to crumble. Down the cobbled side streets there were vistas of hideous tenements in dark red brick. Such shops as there were had neither brightness nor attraction. Every few hundred yards we passed groups of muffled road sweepers, mostly women, dourly attacking the hummocky, hard-packed ice with picks and shovels and drills. There were noisy trams in linked twos and threes, some drawing flatcars of freight behind them, besieged at every stop by milling crowds and moving off with clusters of people clinging desperately to the doors and each other, like flies on a carcass. There were bleak open spaces, piled with timber stacks and heaps of gray snow that had still to be removed. Nowhere was there any color or light. In my cheerless mood, I almost regretted that I'd agreed to come back to this big and ugly city, that seemed to be growing uglier week by week.

It was a passing feeling. My spirits rose as the green turrets of the Kremlin came into sight and the taxi approached the older district of Arbat. The residential streets there, tree-lined and quiet, still had some elegance; and the house where I lived—the home of a former Moscow merchant—was dignified and comfortable. I shared it with three other newspapermen—George Miles, of the London *Dispatch,* and two Americans, Slattery and Logan. It was a place we'd taken over already furnished and it was full of red plush and antimacassars and potted evergreen plants and Victorian bric-a-brac. It was spacious but warm, for it had double doors at the entrance and its double windows, like all windows in Moscow, had been sealed with strips of paper in the autumn to keep out drafts. Only a tiny ventilating pane in each room, called a *fortushka,* now admitted any air, but at least the stuffiness could be controlled. As a place to live in, the house was infinitely more comfortable than a hotel, and it had the great advantage that we didn't have to waste hours every day trying to get service. We had our own rooms, as well as a communal sitting room and dining room, and we were looked after by a buxom, middle-aged woman named Katya, who cleaned conscientiously and cooked well and only occasionally stole our shirts and shaving cream. It was quite a snug arrangement.

No one but Slattery was in when I arrived. He was a lean, athletic man in his mid-thirties, a native of New Jersey who covered for a syndicate.

"Well, if it isn't the Senator!" he said, with a grin of welcome. "We weren't expecting you till tomorrow."

"I caught an earlier plane," I told him. "I couldn't resist the pull of the place any longer."

"I'll bet! Anyway, it's nice to see you back, Tim. Did you have a good leave?"

"Fine," I lied. Maybe some day I'd feel like talking to

someone about Marya, but not yet. I dropped into a high-backed armchair, flanked by an aspidistra, and relaxed. "What's new, Joe?"

"Nothing you wouldn't know about. . . . Except we've got mice."

"No!"

"It's a fact. Katya's put something down, but they keep gobbling it up and coming back for more. . . . Oh, and we had the Ghanaians, demonstrating in Red Square about their treatment. I thought we were the only guys who ever answered back in this town, but *they* sure did. Boy, was it a riot!"

"Yes, I read about it. . . . Tell me, how's Pavlov?" Rodion Pavlov was the top man at the Press Department of the Soviet Foreign Ministry and our main official contact for all purposes.

"Oh, he's pretty affable right now. . . . Helping the thaw along, I guess."

"Good. . . . I've got to try and wheedle a winter trip out of him. . . . My editor's set his heart on a series of feature articles."

"That so? Well, you might be lucky—they seem anxious to please. . . . Where are you thinking of going?"

"All round the Ukraine."

"M'm—sounds like you're in for a long wait. . . . Why don't you come skiing with Cy and me till they fix it?" Cy was Logan—the correspondent of the *New York Star*. "We're off to the Carpathians in a fortnight. Christmas in the mountains."

"Nice," I said. "But then *you* haven't just had six weeks' leave. It'll be Christmas at the Nark for me. . . ." The "Nark" was our name for the Soviet Foreign Ministry. Years back, the department had been known as Narkomindyel, the Russian abbreviation for People's Commissariat for Foreign Affairs—and because "Nark" had a slightly derogatory sound, the name had stuck.

I picked up my suitcase. "Well, I suppose I'd better go and get unpacked."

"Bring any Scotch, Senator?"

"Three bottles."

"Oh, jolly good show! We'll have a celebration tonight."

"You bet," I said.

I wished I could think of something to celebrate.

First thing next morning I rang the Nark and asked for an appointment with Pavlov. The secretary, Nina Alexandrovna, was friendly, but vague about his movements. "I will let you know, Lord Quainton, when he will be free. Probably it will be tomorrow."

That suited me well. I gave a cursory glance at the morning papers to make sure nothing sensational had happened overnight. Then I dug out my black astrakhan hat, my Russian overcoat with the astrakhan collar, and my shiny Russian briefcase, and set out on foot for the Lenin Library in Mokhovaya Street, wearing my Russian shoes and galoshes. In that rig I looked more like a Soviet functionary than a foreigner. I'd often found that it smoothed the way in minor inquiries.

The pavements were covered with knobs and ridges of ice and were very treacherous, but I soon rediscovered the wary, slithering step I'd learned over the years, and I made good progress. There were quite a lot of people about—women with hand-sleighs and baskets on their way to GUM, the big store; men with parcels and attaché cases on interminable errands from office to office; militiamen nonchalantly smoking and occasionally blowing their whistles at erring pedestrians. Almost all the passers-by had expressionless faces and a total lack of challenge or interest in their eyes. These blank street faces would never cease to baffle me. Looking at them, it was hard to believe that the Russians, when personally aroused, could be about the most vital people in the world.

The weather had brightened and walking was pleasant—particularly as I was making for the one picturesque spot in Moscow. Ahead of me lay the granite-lined curve of the Moskva river, now frozen into stillness; the Kremlin with its delicate pink walls and green-topped towers and golden domes; the quaint onion-stripes of St. Basil's; and Red Square, with its line of patient pilgrims queuing at the Mausoleum. It was a museum piece, but an ever-fascinating one, and I took it all in appreciatively before turning off along Mokhovaya. I paused for a moment to let a squad of bosomy Red army girls go by, singing their heads off; then committed myself to a vast square with twelve traffic lanes and hardly any pedestrian islands, pursued by the noise of a raucous loud-speaker exhorting me to buy State bonds. The crossing wasn't the suicidal adventure it might have been, because in fact there was only enough traffic for two lanes, and the greatest hazard proved to be a group of small boys rolling a big log home.

In twenty minutes I reached the Lenin Library—a plain, rectangular building spoiled by a row of silhouetted statues on its roof that positively clamored for target practice. I'd been to the library serveral times before, because it was one of the few places in Moscow where you could get hold of a reference book, and I knew my way around it fairly well. What I didn't know was whether they kept back files of newspapers. It turned out that they did, but the girl librarian wasn't sure how far back the files of *Vechernaya Moskva* went. I could understand her doubt, for it was a paper of no great significance or standing—which made it all the more puzzling that it alone had carried a report of the Raczinski trial.

I filled in a form and sat down to wait. I waited for a little over half an hour. Then the girl reappeared, dusty but triumphant, and slapped a file down in front of me. I thanked her, and turned to the issue of June 11th, 1953. I didn't expect to dig up anything useful out of the dead ashes of Loda. I just wanted to see what had been said in court.

I soon found the piece I was looking for. There was a big headline—THREE MORE WAR MISCREANTS BROUGHT TO ACCOUNT. The story was a characteristic example of Soviet reporting—masses of verbiage, with only the tiniest kernel of fact. It seemed that the special court—about which no details were given, not even the date on which it had met—had tried two other men besides the one they called Raczinski—one Russian and one Ukrainian. They had both been charged with beating prisoners at Loda, and both had been sentenced to death.

Evidence against Raczinski had been given by two Russians who said they had been at the camp with him. Their names were Ivan Phillipovitch Lutkin and Pavel Alexandrovitch Skaliga. According to their statements, they had both overheard him disclosing to a camp guard the existence of an escape plot. As a result, all the men concerned in the plot had been executed. No one, it seemed, had asked the two witnesses any questions, and no details of their evidence had been reported. Judgment had been pronounced at once.

That was all—and precious little it was. . . . Still, I didn't think my trek to the library had been entirely a waste of time.

I spent the afternoon at my desk in Arbat with a rather inadequate map, doing what I'd started to do at the London office the day I'd found the clipping, but had never finished—sketch out a provisional itinerary for the Ukraine trip so that I'd have something specific to put before Pavlov. I indicated the main places I had in mind—substantially those I'd mentioned to Cole—with a note about the purpose of each call and a rough estimate of the amount of time I thought each might need. Pavlov would no doubt have different ideas if he ever got around to considering the matter, but at least this would give him something to work on. I also typed out a formal request for the trip on letterhead paper of the *Sunday Recorder* and signed the letter over a special rubber stamp I'd had made. You don't get anywhere in Russia without a special rubber stamp. Later in the afternoon Nina Alexandrovna rang me to say I could have an appointment at ten in the morning, and I said I'd be there.

Sharp on the hour next day I arrived at the Nark—a resplendent new building in Sadovaya Ring. Formerly, the Foreign Ministry had been housed in Bolshaya Lubianka, close by the headquarters of the security police and only a stone's throw from the Lubianka prison—a juxtaposition which must have been most convenient in the days of Stalin's purges, when Soviet diplomats were melting away like ice in the sun. But now all was chromium, modern, and apparently civilized. I showed my pass at the door, left my coat, hat, scarf, gloves, and galoshes in the vestibule—wearing outdoor clothes indoors in Russia is regarded as the height of bad manners, like whistling—and went through into the outer office where Nina presided. She was a handsome girl in her late twenties—a tall, dark Leningrader, and one of the few women in Russia I'd ever seen wearing a really good suit. By nature she was a kind and helpful person, and she always did her best to make up in personal willingness for the appalling red tape and inefficiency of the department she served. She gave me a smiling welcome and said Mr. Pavlov wouldn't be long. In fact I waited only twenty minutes, which was almost a record for speed. Then a bell rang on her desk and she asked me to go in.

Rodion Pavlov was a good-looking and highly intelligent man of about forty with whom I'd always had excellent relations at the personal level. He was dark and dapper in appearance; he dressed immaculately in black jacket and striped trousers; and he always managed to maintain a front of unruffled courtesy. A meeting with him could develop quickly into a fencing match, and often it did, but if he ever became unpleasant it was only in the subtlest way. He seemed marked out for very high office in the Soviet diplomatic hierarchy, and I suspected that in his quiet way he already enjoyed considerable influence.

He rose from his leather armchair as I entered and greeted me with a cordial handshake. "Welcome back, Lord Quainton. . . . I hope you enjoyed your holiday."

I said I had.

"Good. . . ." He offered me a cigarette, which I politely declined. Russian cigarettes have tobacco at one end and cardboard at the other, and to me both ends taste alike. "So you're probably going to be with us for at least another year?"

"That seems to be the idea."

He smiled. "You still prefer journalism to sitting in the House of Lords and making speeches?"

"I think so. At the moment, anyway."

"Well, your Parliament's loss is our gain. . . ." He waved me to a chair and resumed his seat. "Now what are your plans? Is there any way in which I can be of help to you?"

"There is indeed," I said. I told him about the trip I hoped to make. I emphasized that the *Recorder* was prepared to give a lot of space to it. I explained fully the idea behind it, since lack of frankness now would only recoil on me later. "It's a question of winter efficiency," I said. "Obviously, one doesn't expect miracles. You and I both know that there's some stagnation, some waste, because of the weather. For that matter, there is in England when we have a cold snap. But there must be many new techniques, many enterprises with new methods. My aim would be to present a factual, balanced report of what I found."

"That, Lord Quainton, you always manage to achieve. As you know, we hold you in the highest esteem as a reporter. . . ." He was silent for a while, weighing the project. "Where had you thought of going?"

I passed him the rough schedule I'd drawn up, and he glanced through it. "Yes—I see. . . . Quite an ambitious trip. . . . It would require, I should think, at least a month from start to finish."

"At least. . . . Perhaps six weeks."

"And, in midwinter, it would need to be organized with the greatest care, otherwise it could be very uncomfortable. Transportation, stopping places, facilities—everything would have to be fixed up in advance."

"Well, you've always been very good at that," I said.

His dark eyes sparkled. "I've heard less complimentary opinions from some of your colleagues, Lord Quainton. But no doubt we could arrange something. . . . Anyhow, I'll see what can be done and I'll let you know."

It was as much as I'd hoped for, and I thanked him. "Now there is one other thing," I said. "It's a personal matter—and rather a delicate one."

He inclined his head. "I can be very discreet."

"I'm afraid it's not your discretion I'm asking for, Mr. Pavlov, but your assistance. . . . While I was on leave, I met a girl whom I hope to marry."

"Indeed. . . . My felicitations."

"Her name is Marya Raczinski."

"A Russian girl?"

"No—a British subject, but a former Pole. . . . Everything was going well. . . . Then, a few days ago, I discovered that her father, Stefan Raczinski, had been condemned in absentia as a war criminal—by a Soviet court."

Pavlov's face fell. "Oh, dear," he said. "I'm very sorry to hear that. Very sorry indeed. . . . When was this—condemnation?"

"In 1953. . . ." I outlined the facts as I knew them. He listened gravely.

"Most unfortunate," he said. "Most unpleasant for you—a great shock. . . . You have my sincere sympathy. . . . But how do you think I can help you?"

I chose my words carefully, knowing that a wrong nuance would abruptly end our talk. "Naturally," I said, "I'm not questioning for a moment the verdict of the court on the man who was found guilty. . . . What I'm wondering is whether, by any chance, there could have been some mistake of identity. A mistake in the name, perhaps—or a mistake in identifying the particular Raczinski concerned. All in complete good faith."

Pavlov eyed me thoughtfully. "Have you any reason to think such a mistake might have been made?"

"Well, to start with, I've met Raczinski. I don't know

him well, but I can't see him as the sort of man who would betray his fellow prisoners. It's an exceptionally vile thing to do—and to my mind he doesn't fit the role."

"A subjective judgment, of course," Pavlov said. "If you planned to marry his daugher, you would naturally wish to think the best of him."

"I accept that. . . . But there are other things. So far as I could see from the report in *Vechernaya Moskva,* the two witnesses didn't describe the Raczinski they were referring to. That does seem to leave open the possibility of error. . . . Then again, Stefan Raczinski made no attempt to change his name, or to conceal the fact that he'd been at Loda. To me, that suggests a clear conscience, not guilt."

"It could have been exceptional cleverness on his part, Lord Quainton. If he had changed his name and not mentioned Loda, and then by chance had met someone in England who had been at the camp and remembered him—as he might well have done—he would have found it much more difficult to rebut any charge. He might have preferred what seemed the lesser risk—apparent frankness."

It was a point I hadn't thought of, and it rather took the wind from my sails.

"All the same," I said, "I think a mistake is possible."

Pavlov gave a faint shrug. "Anyone can make a mistake—we are all human. . . . I have no definite opinion myself in this matter because I am entirely unfamiliar with it. . . . What exactly are you asking me to do?"

"I'm asking you," I said, "as a great personal favor to me, to look into the case. I have the names of the two witnesses. If they could be found, they could be asked to describe Raczinski. I have a photograph of him here. It might be that they would say at once that he wasn't the man. . . . I realize that I'm asking a great deal—that there's nothing at stake but the happiness of one or two people. . . ."

"Happiness in not unimportant, Lord Quainton. Nor is justice. But we must be practical. All this, you say, occurred some ten years ago. The witnesses may well be dead. Even if they are alive, they may be anywhere in Russia—and the Soviet Union is a big place. It would be hard to find them."

"With your resources, I think you could do it."

Pavlov shook his head doubtfully. "Our resources have many calls on them. . . . And if we were able to find the witnesses, I think it very likely that the man they described would prove to be your Stefan Raczinski. Then where would you be?"

"I'm prepared to take that risk," I said. "All I want is to be convinced of the truth—whatever it is."

"I understand. Well, I will make some inquiries. Obviously I can guarantee nothing—but I would like to feel that you were satisfied. . . . What was it your great jurist said—'Justice must not only be done—it must be seen to be done.' "

If I hadn't needed Pavlov's help so badly, I'd have greeted that remark with a belly laugh. Coming from an official of a ruthless police state, it was undoubtedly the joke of the year. . . . As it was, I just smiled.

I'd carried the inquiry forward in the only way I could but I'd no illusions that I'd made any great progress. If Raczinski was right, and the Russians had made a mistake about him and knew it, they weren't at all likely to want to reopen the case—and the chances were I'd hear no more. If they didn't think they'd made a mistake it seemed unlikely they'd go to the trouble of looking into it again for my sake—thaw or no thaw. Pavlov's personal friendliness certainly didn't mean that action would be taken, because it wouldn't be he who made the final decision. However, the Russians *were* unpredictable. For the obscurest of motives, they sometimes made the most surprising gestures. It was much too soon to give up hope. . . .

That night, I wrote to Marya. It wasn't easy, and I made several false starts. I didn't think that emotion would influence her much in her present mood, and I doubted if argument would. That didn't leave a great deal. The version I finally sent read, in part:

I wonder if you have had any second thoughts about our situation? As far as I'm concerned—as I told your father before I left—I simply refuse to accept that anything has changed. In the diplomatic phrase, I'm "rejecting" your note. I understand why you wrote it, but you're attributing feelings to me that I just don't have. I won't go over all the old ground again now, because if I couldn't bring you to see things my way when we were lovingly together, it's unlikely that I can persuade you in a letter. What I hope, and shall go on hoping, is that time will soften your extreme attitude. I just can't accept that with so much love and understanding between us, such depth of feeling as we both have, it's either necessary or right that our relationship should be cut off so brutally. I wish you hadn't rushed away as you did. After all, we're both fairly intelligent and sensible people, and discussion—even if it doesn't seem to be getting anywhere at the time—is more likely to build a bridge than separation. You said you hoped I wouldn't be angry—but I am, about that, and I think I've a right to be. Anyway, this is just to let you know that my own feelings haven't changed and that I still plan to come back at Easter and marry you!

About your father—I've started to make a few inquiries here. I hasten to add that this isn't because I need to resolve any doubts—since, as I told you, I don't have any—but because it's what you seem to want. I can't honestly say I've made much progress so far, but I have made some, and there's just an outside chance that I may be able to *prove* a mistake was made. I'll let you know the moment I have any news.

Please write to me, Marya. I think of you always, and I miss you terribly. The thought that I might lose you for no good reason is quite unendurable. It seems utterly crazy to me that we should condemn ourselves to so much present unhappiness in order to avoid a future problem which isn't at all likely to arise and which really exists only in your imagination.

For the moment, there was nothing more I could do about Marya. In the days that followed, I concentrated on taking up the old threads of the Moscow life and trying to be an adequate correspondent. That wasn't easy in a country where asking unauthorized questions about anything significant was regarded as a form of spying. There might be a slight thaw at the official level but it certainly hadn't removed the basic difficulties of the job. The wind of change that was supposed to be blowing over Russia, lightening restrictions and lifting fear from the people, was no more than a moving coolness when a correspondent tried to make and nourish contacts with ordinary Russians. Maybe it was true that they weren't any longer liable to be picked up by the dicks for associating with a foreigner, but a lot of them preferred not to risk it, and one couldn't blame them.

In the absence of normal personal contacts, routine was a big part of life. There were the Russian papers to sift through each morning on the off-chance of a news story; the propaganda handouts from the Nark to glance at and throw away; the service messages from London to cope with; the diplomatic parties to attend. Occasionally there were visiting politicians, American and British, who were only too ready to be interviewed; sometimes there were delegations to keep an eye on. There were officially arranged meetings with Soviet personalities whose achievements the authorities wanted to publicize; there were rare visits to Soviet institutions; and, very infrequently, there were high-level press conferences.

It wasn't an onerous job, and time sometimes hung heavily. On quiet evenings I would often sit around with Slattery and Logan and Miles, playing gin rummy, drinking whatever was available, and interminably chewing over the Russian scene. We were broadly noncompetitive, so if any of us happened to have any special information we rarely held it back. There were few scoops in Moscow, and those there were would hardly have been recognized as such by the layman. We had frequent arguments, especially when there was some Anglo-American split over policy, but they rarely went very deep. By and large we all felt we were in a hostile country, and the knowledge kept us close. It was a curious, inbred sort of life—physically comfortable, professionally often frustrating—yet all the time there was an underlying excitement, a feeling that at any moment we might find ourselves at the center of the next international earthquake.

The days passed, and I heard nothing more about the Ukraine trip. For all I knew, Pavlov might be working on it like a beaver—or he might be doing nothing at all. In a week or two, I decided, I'd remind him—drop him a note, or seek another interview. Not that it would do any good, if the policy decision had gone against me. I'd be better off going to the ballet or skiing in Sokolniki Park than drafting reasoned appeals. . . .

Then, scarcely more than a week after my return, I had a phone call from Nina asking me to go at once to the Nark to see Pavlov. Her tone of urgency was so unusual that I felt sure it must be about the trip. But it wasn't. It was about the witnesses.

"It seems you were right about our resources, Lord Quainton," Pavlov said with a smile, after we'd exchanged the usual courtesies. "Apparently the old addresses of these two men had been filed away, and tracing their subsequent movements was less difficult than I'd feared. . . . Are you still sure you wish to take the risk?"

"Quite sure," I said.

"Very well. . . . The witness Skaliga, I'm afraid, will be no help at all—I gather he has just been discharged from an inebriates' home in Moscow and is in no condition to describe anything—except perhaps a circle! But the other man, Lutkin, is fit and well, and is working in Tula."

"Tula?" That was only half a day's rail journey south of Moscow. "Then perhaps I could go and see him?"

"In the circumstances," Pavlov said, "we would be prepared to bring him to Moscow. In the interest of better understanding, and as a mark of our esteem for you."

It seemed an extraordinary gesture of goodwill—but at that moment I was too excited by the prospect that had opened up to bother about their motive. "Thank you very much, Mr. Pavlov. I'm most grateful."

"Would three o'clock tomorrow afternoon be convenient for you for an interview? In this office?"

"Perfectly."

"Then that is settled. . . . Until tomorrow, Lord Quainton."

Hopefully, I was at the Nark on the dot of three next day. There was a disquieting lack of activity around the place and I wasn't surprised when Nina greeted me with apologies on Pavlov's behalf and explained that the Tula train would be a little late. A car had been sent to the station and would rush Lutkin to the Ministry immediately he arrived. Would I mind waiting?

I'd brought a book with me and I settled down to read. I did a lot of my serious reading at the Nark. Nothing happened until nearly four, and then there were footsteps in the corridor and a little man with a briefcase came in and said rather breathlessly that his name was Lutkin. He was about fifty years old, wore thick glasses, and had the look of an office worker in a fairly humble position. Nina spoke on the phone and Pavlov came out. He shook hands with me, regretting the delay; shook hands with Lutkin; and led the way into his room, where we all took seats.

There was a little pause as Pavlov and I both studied Lutkin. Then Pavlov said, "You are Ivan Phillipovitch Lutkin?" Lutkin nodded. "This is Lord Quainton, a British newspaper correspondent." Lutkin nodded again, to me. He was clutching his briefcase tightly in his lap and looked rather nervous.

Pavlov addressed him again. "You were once in Loda camp, Comrade Lutkin, is that right? In 1953 you gave evidence in a Moscow court together with Pavel Alexandrovitch Skaliga, against a man named Raczinski who was not then present?"

"That is correct," Lutkin said.

"So. . . . Now Lord Quainton wishes to ask you some questions. Please answer them to the best of your ability." Pavlov gestured to me. "You have the floor, Lord Quainton. Ask anything you wish."

I said, "How long were you in Loda camp, Mr. Lutkin?"

"About three months."

"Was this man you accused also there for the whole of that time?"

"No, only for the last three or four weeks. . . . He was brought in shortly before the camp was liberated by our glorious Red army."

"As a prisoner?"

"Yes."

"Where exactly did you meet him?"

"He was in the same hut as Skaliga and myself."

"I see. . . . Now how did you come to overhear his conversation with the German guard?"

"Skaliga and I were walking to the toilet block. As we approached it we heard voices inside. A man was speaking of an escape plan from our hut. He stopped talking as we entered. It was Raczinski. The other man was a guard. . . . Afterwards, fifteen men were taken from our hut and shot."

"Did Raczinski come back to the hut?"

"No, I didn't see him again. No doubt he was removed for protection."

"Did you know of this escape plan yourself?"

"No—I wasn't approached."

"*Was* there a plan?"

"Oh, yes, there was one. I learned about it afterward."

"What language was Raczinski speaking when you overheard him?"

Lutkin frowned. "I think it was German."

"You understand German?"

"Yes, quite well. . . ."

"Now how did you know this man's name was Raczinski?"

"He told us."

"When he first came to the hut?"

"Yes."

"Did you hear his first name?"

"Yes—Stefan."

"Did you call him Raczinski, or Stefan?"

Lutkin blinked at me. "I didn't call him anvthing. I didn't talk to him much. Nor did anyone. From the first he was not popular. There was something about him. . . ."

"In that case," I said, "you may only have heard his name once or twice during the three weeks or so he was with you?"

"It's possible."

"Then are you quite sure his name *was* Raczinski?"

"That was the name he gave."

"Did you ever see it written down?"

"No."

"You merely heard it, just once or twice. . . . Could you not have been mistaken in the name? Could it not have been, say, Ravinsky or Radetsky?"

Lutkin hesitated. "I think it was Raczinski."

Pavlov, who had been following the dialogue with close attention, said sharply, "This is very important, Comrade Lutkin. Thinking is not enough. Are you sure of the name, or are you not?"

Lutkin seemed to shrink into his chair. "It's a long time ago, Comrade Pavlov. More than twenty years. I am sure of what happened—it is etched into my mind forever. But the exact name—a slight difference in sound—that is another matter."

For the first time, Pavlov looked disturbed. "I see. . . . Go on, Lord Quainton."

I turned again to Lutkin. "This man," I said, "this Radetsky or Ravinsky or Raczinski . . . Can you describe him?"

Lutkin stared down at the floor. "I will try. . . . He was a fairly tall man, I think. . . . At least, of medium height. . . . And of average build. . . . A youngish man. . . ."

"How young?"

"That is hard to say. . . . Perhaps thirty—perhaps a little less."

"What was his face like? Was it fat, thin, ugly, scarred. . . ? Can you remember anything of his features?"

"I have a bad memory for faces, *gospodeen*—and it is so long ago. . . . But I think he was quite good-looking."

"What about his head? Was there anything special about its shape?"

"I seem to remember he had rather a big head."

Pavlov intervened again. "You must try to be more specific, Comrad Lutkin. Was it long? Was it broad?"

Lutkin quailed. "Just—big. . . . I am sorry, Comrade Pavlov, that I cannot be more sure. At the trial no one asked me these things."

I produced the photograph of Raczinski and passed it to him. "Is that the man?"

He held it close to his face, peering at it through his bulbous lenses. There was a long silence. "Yes," he said at last, "I think . . ." He broke off. "He was younger then, of course. . . . It could be. . . ." Slowly, he shook his head. "To be honest, I am not sure. . . ."

"Let me see it," Pavlov said. He took the photograph and studied it. After a moment he said, "I would not think this was a face it was easy to forget—not once you had seen it. The high forehead is quite exceptional."

"It was a long while ago," Lutkin repeated. "And I have a bad memory for people."

Pavlov turned coldly away from him. "Have you any more questions, Lord Quainton?"

I shook my head.

"Then you may leave, Comrade Lutkin. The car which brought you will take you to the station."

Lutkin got up, dropped his briefcase, and retrieved it. He looked very shaken. "Will there be trouble, Comrade Pavlov. . . ? Everything I told the court was true."

"Of course there will be no trouble," Pavlov said. "You did your best. Thank you for coming." He opened the door and let Lutkin out.

His face was solemn as he turned back to me. "Well—that was a most disconcerting interview, Lord Quainton."

"It was a most interesting one," I said.

"For me, surprising—and very disquieting. . . . What a pity it is that your Raczinski could not have presented himself here for identification."

"Before the trial," I said, "he knew nothing about it. After the trial, he'd been sentenced to ten years' imprisonment. Would *you* have come?"

Pavlov gave a wintry smile. "Perhaps I was being a little unrealisitc. . . . Anyhow, Lord Quainton, what is your feeling now?"

"Naturally, I think more than ever that a mistake was made."

"Yes, I can understand that. It certainly seems possible. . . . But this negative evidence of Lutkin, this failure of memory, is far from conclusive. The opposite possibility still exists. . . . Quite frankly, I can hold out no hope that the case will be officially reopened."

"I don't expect that."

"You mean that you are satisfied?"

"I'm certainly not going to waste energy crying for the moon. Why should I? Raczinski himself isn't worried—he always thought it was a case of mistaken identity. I thought so too. The difficulty was to make his daughter believe that I thought so. Now I hope to do just that."

Pavlov looked relieved. "Well, I certainly hope you succeed, Lord Quainton. I do sincerely hope so."

"Thank you," I said. "I'm most indebted to you for all you've done."

"I certainly didn't expect to be of service. I was quite sure the interview would go the other way. . . . But for your sake, I'm glad that it didn't. . . . Now is there anything more I can do for you?"

"The trip?" I said hopefully.

"The trip—ah, yes. I am working on that, and you will hear something very soon. . . . Good-bye, Lord Quainton."

I left the Nark in a bit of a daze. It all seemed too good to be true.

I walked back to Arbat feeling more cheerful than at any time since the start of the Raczinski trouble. It really did seem as though, against all expectations, I'd as good as proved that the wrong man had been condemned —and I couldn't see how even the ultrasensitive Marya could have anything more to worry about. She'd demanded certainty and I *was* certain—on very good grounds. All I had to do now was write and tell her about the Lutkin interview and our difficulties should be over. . . .

It was only when I started to rehearse in my mind the actual details of the letter I'd send that I began to feel a little less satisfied about the adequacy of the interview. Marya would obviously want to know exactly what Lutkin had said—and she'd rely on me to tell her the truth. I'd have to say that on two points—big head and good looks— his description could have fitted Raczinski, and that on one—rather tall—he'd been a bit wide of the mark. Otherwise, as Pavlov had said, he'd been inconclusive and negative. Was that good enough? It would have been fine if he'd confidently described a completely different man, or if he'd turned down the photograph out of hand. But in fact he'd simply been unsure. . . .

And why? Well, for one thing he'd been in a state of jitters because of having to answer my questions in the presence of high officialdom. I wished, now, that I could have seen him alone, and informally. I'd have taken the interview at a quieter pace, and in the end I'd probably have been able to get much more out of him. . . .

Another thing was the state of his eyes. He'd seemed half blind to me, and it was possible he'd never clearly seen the face he'd called Raczinski's. If he'd been like that for long, it wasn't surprising he was bad at remembering people. . . . Up to a point the interview had been reassuring—but suddenly it began to look to me as though I'd done only half a job.

I began to wonder then about the other witness—Skaliga. A compulsive drunk might prove no more reliable than a myopic when it came to descriptions—but drunks did have their lucid moments. Now if I could see him—preferably on his own—and he turned out to have normal recollections *and* rejected the photograph, that really would be conclusive. . . . But what were my chances of finding him—without calling in the authorities again and getting saddled with another office interview. . . ?

I was still thinking about it as I reached the house. There, for a while, other things claimed my attention. There was a frightful noise coming from the sitting room —an unusually bibulous noise for that time in the evening. Slattery, Logan, and Miles were all there, drinking vodka. Logan was stretched out on the settee—a position I'd never known him to adopt in the daytime, unless he had a blonde with him. He was a large, powerful man, an amateur heavyweight. From the door, only his crisp, curly hair and his slightly flattened nose were visible. And his glass —which he waved in greeting.

"What's this?" I said. "A celebration?"

"Not on your bloody life, Senator," Logan called. "It's a wake."

"A *wake*. . . ? Someone dead?"

"Yes—my foot." He raised a heavily bandaged leg.

"Oh, lord!" I exclaimed. "Anything serious?"

"They say not. . . . Just enough to bitc hthings up for the rest of the winter. We're drowning our sorrows."

I looked at Slattery. "No ski trip, eh?"

"Not for Cy. . . . There's just a chance I may be able to fix something up with Ed Schwartz."

"Well, I call that damn bad luck. . . . How did you do it, Cy?"

"Fell down a crevasse in one of the icefields they call a street. . . ." He held out his glass. "Fill me up, will you, Senator?"

I poured him out a shot, and one for myself. "Anyone here know anything about homes for alcoholics in Moscow?" I asked.

"Now wait a minute. . . !" Cy began.

"Nothing personal," I said. "This is on the level. . . . I want to see a man who's just come out of one."

"He wants to see a man about the hair of a dog," Miles said, with a chuckle. Miles was a kindly, gentle character who sometimes got a bit childish in his cups.

"What's the guy's name?" Slattery asked.

"Skaliga."

Slattery repeated the name. "That's a new one on me. I'd guess there couldn't be many of those around in the town."

"No," I agreed. "Not that it helps. . . ." In any normal city I'd have looked up an unusual name like that in the telephone directory as a first step, but Moscow didn't have a telephone directory—not a published one. It was one of their security measures—I suppose they thought it helped to make the bureaucrats more inaccessible. You could always ring "Inquiries"—but if you wanted to keep your business quiet it was better not to.

Slattery said: "What makes you think he's been in a home?"

"I was told."

"Reliable source?"

"Not very."

Miles said, "I've got some dope I picked up at the Health Ministry last year—there might be something in that. . . . Half a mo, I'll get it."

He went off upstairs. In a few moments he was back with a thick, duplicated typescript. "Here you are—a hundred thousand crisp words on keeping fit in the workers' paradise. Read all about it."

"Thanks," I said, "you're a pal." I sat down by the phone and paged through the typescript. It was crude propaganda stuff, but it covered the ground. Sure enough, there was a section on "The War against Alcoholism"—and three "curative centers" in Moscow were mentioned.

That opened a chink. Miles had the Health Ministry's number in a notebook, and I rang them. I said I was an author who wanted to write about "The War against Alcoholism," and could they give me the telephone numbers of the three establishments mentioned in their literature, so that I could make appointments. I was going to hang up if they showed any curiosity about me, but they didn't. They just gave me the numbers.

I phoned the first one and asked for the secretariat. "My name is Leo Popov," I said, quelling with a glance—or trying to—a guffaw from Cy. "*Dr.* Popov. . . . I've just flown in from the Lenin hospital in Alma Ata and I'm looking for a former patient of mine named Pavel Alexandrovitch Skaliga. I understand he's recently been discharged from your institution, but he isn't at his old address. Can you tell me, please, the address he was discharged to?"

I drew a blank at the first place—they hadn't heard of him. I said I must have been misinformed about the institution he'd gone to, and rang off. I then got two wrong numbers in succession and had an altercation with the operator. All telephone systems are infuriating, but the Moscow one is in a class by itself. Finally I was put through to the second place on my list. They looked up the name—and they found it. I'd wondered at the Nark if that inebriate business had been some sort of excuse—but it wasn't. Skaliga had been discharged, they said, about two weeks ago. The address he'd given was Flat 6, House 4, Mali Pereulok. I repeated it, and put the receiver down with a feeling of considerable achievement.

"Going slumming, eh?" Miles said. "I've been to Mali Pereulok—it's a terrible place."

"You know what," Slattery said, to no one in particular. "For a respectable lord, that guy has quite a technique. 'My name is Leo Popov. *Dr*. Popov. . . . I've just flown in from Alma Ata.' " His mimicry, even in Russian, wasn't bad. "Don't know how he thinks of it—off the cuff, too. And such authority!"

I grinned. "You know what they say. Love will find a way."

"What's that supposed to mean?"

"One day I'll tell you."

Cy held out his glass again. "You'll end up in the Lubianka, bud. . . . Give me another shot, while you're still free."

Directly after dinner I changed into an old padded jacket and trousers that I sometimes used on trips, slipped a half liter of vodka into each side pocket, and set off for Mali Pereulok on the eastern outskirts of the city. I wore a black leather hat with turned-down earflaps, and the spacious felt boots that the Russians call *valinki*. It was an outfit that wouldn't catch the eye of the *dvornik* at House 4, if he was around.

I took a trolley bus across town. At that time of night the bus was comparatively empty—that's to say, there was almost no one actually clinging to the outside of it. Inside was jam-packed and looked impenetrable, but I'd learned the drill for getting through, and off at the right place. The moment I'd gained a foothold by the back door I started to fight my way toward the front one, which was the exit. At some point I gave my fare to a neighbor to be passed over a score of heads to the conductress, which was the only way anyone ever paid a fare in Moscow. The ticket never reached me. At two road junctions the trolley bounced off the wire and the girl driver had to shin up a ladder on to the roof and sort out the chaos single-handed in a shower of sparks. Otherwise the journey was uneventful.

I'd checked with a street map, and I got out a couple of

hundred yards from Mali Pereulok, at a point where the trolley-bus route turned off. It was, as Miles had said, a wretched district—a bleak main road with dilapidated pavements and bad lighting and sinister side streets lined with ancient tenement blocks. Mali Pereulok proved to be one of the darkest turnings, for most of the bulbs had been removed from the street lamps. I narrowly escaped falling down an unguarded sewer manhole which had been left open for snow to be pushed into it, and I cursed myself for not having brought a torch. It took me quite a while to find House 4. When, finally, I did, I pushed through the paintless double doors and climbed the bare concrete stairway as though I were a resident. There was no sign of the house porter. The air smelt of dirt and old clothes and neglected lavatories and the cheap home-grown tobacco, *makhorka*. It was horrible, but familiar.

I found Flat 6 on the third floor, and knocked. My worst fear was that Skaliga wouldn't be in and that I'd have to repeat the journey. But I could hear voices. I knocked again, and a blowzy woman opened the door. I said, "Is Pavel Alexandr'itch home?" as though I knew him. She screeched an inquiry to someone inside, then nodded and let me into the hall. "That's his room," she said, pointing to a peeling door. I knocked at the door, and someone stirred, and a voice growled "Come in." I went in. The room was about ten feet by twelve. It had three iron bedsteads in it, and two wooden chairs, and a spittoon in a corner, and not much else. A man in undershirt and trousers was stretched out on one of the beds. He sat up as I entered, leaning heavily on one elbow. He was a big, fleshy man of fifty or so, with a sallow, puffy face and bleary eyes. There was an empty tumbler beside him on a wooden box and I smelt vodka—but I couldn't see any around.

"Who are you?" he asked truculently. He wasn't drunk, but he wasn't sober either. He might have been discharged from the Home but he evidently hadn't been discharged cured.

"My name is Quainton," I said. "I'm an English newspaper correspondent. Are you Pavel Alexandrovitch Skaliga?"

"Yes," he said.

"Then I'd like to talk to you about what happened at Loda camp twenty years ago."

He sank back on the bed. "I've nothing to say to you. Get out."

"I talked this afternoon to Ivan Phillipovitch Lutkin at the Ministry of Foreign Affairs," I told him. "It was all official. There's no reason why you shouldn't talk too."

He was in a pretty fuddled state, but he seemed to take that in. He looked at me doubtfully.

"I've come all the way across town," I said, "and it's cold out tonight. Fifteen degrees of frost. . . . At least we could have a drink." I produced the two bottles of vodka.

I could see by the way he eyed them that he wouldn't be able to say no. But he stalled. "You don't look like a correspondent," he said. His speech, though slurred, was educated. He was a hulk now, but he'd seen better days.

"I assure you I am one," I said. I showed him my press card, which had my photograph on it. He glanced at it, and waved it away.

"Well, there's no harm in having a drink," he said. He heaved himself off the bed and found a second glass. He put it beside the other, opened one of the vodka bottles with a practiced tap at its base, poured two stiff shots, and motioned me to take one of the rickety wooden chairs. From a cupboard he produced a piece of black bread, which he broke in halves.

"Your health!" he said. I raised my glass to him and we downed the vodka. He broke off a bit of bread and ate it. I did the same.

"You drink like a Russian," he said.

"I've been in Moscow a long while."

He poured two more shots. "What did you want to ask me about?"

"About a man named Ravinsky or Radetsky who was in the camp with you. You gave evidence against him at a trial in 1953."

"You mean Raczinski. . . ? That bastard?"

I hadn't expected him to come out so pat with the name. Vodka or no, he was much more on the ball than Lutkin had been.

"Are you sure that was his name—Raczinski?"

"You bet I'm sure. There's nothing wrong with my memory." He grinned. "Not when I'm sober."

"Can you describe this man?"

"Of course I can describe him. . . ." He raised his glass again. "Your health!" We went through the routine. What color there was in his face drained away, and I wasn't surprised. I was beginning to feel muzzy myself—and he was refilling the glasses. Obviously I'd got to work fast.

"Then describe him," I said.

"He was a short, stocky man. He had a big head. . . . And a great, high forehead."

I nearly fell off my chair.

"And he'd been shot in the knee. . . ."

I stared at him incredulously. "Shot in the knee?"

"Yes—at the back here. . . ." He demonstrated—just as Raczinski had done. "The bullet missed the bone and went through the muscle. Pity it didn't go through his head."

"But I—I understood he got his wound *after* he left the camp."

"No, *gospodeen,* before. . . . I saw it."

"You mean he showed it to you. . . ? Lutkin said he wasn't popular—that hardly anyone talked to him."

"That's right—but *he* talked to *me*. He tried to make me believe he'd got the wound defending Warsaw, when the Germans first attacked. Making out he was a loyal Pole. Swine!"

I showed him the photograph—though it hardly seemed necessary now. "Is that the man?"

He gave it one glance. "That's Raczinski. . . . Only he

looked younger then. . . . See the high forehead?" He gazed at me with sudden suspicion. "You know him?"

"I've met him."

"If *I* met him," Skaliga said, "I'd break his neck. . . . You're sure he's not a friend of yours?"

"I wouldn't call him a friend."

"Good. . . . Your health, then. . . . *Do kontsa.*" Once more we drained glasses. Skaliga opened the second bottle and poured two more shots. They looked like four to me. "You know what he did. . . ?"

I struggled to remember. "Lutkin said he betrayed an escape plan. That you overheard him talking to a guard."

"Yes, in the lavatory."

"What language was he talking?"

"German, *gospodeen,* German. . . ."

"Do you understand German?"

"Enough. . . . You might not think so now, but I went to University. . . . He was talking fast—but I understood."

"You mean he was fluent?"

"He was talking like a German. I think he *was* a German. A spy, sent to the camp to listen. . . . I saw him once, afterward, laughing and joking with the guards. After the prisoners had been shot."

"He told me he was a Pole," I said.

"You can't believe a word that bastard says. . . . He was a German all right." Skaliga reached for his glass, missed it, clutched it. "Your health, *gospodeen.*"

I drank, and staggered to my feet. "I must go. . . ."

He was suddenly truculent again. "Not yet . . . There's more in the bottle. . . ."

I blundered past him to the door, and out through the hall to the stairs. My head and my thoughts were whirling. In the street, I was violently sick.

To this day, I'm still not quite sure how I got home. I suppose I walked. I have a vague recollection of falling on my bed, where I must have passed out cold. Next morning I was in a horrible state. I woke with only the slenderest attachment to life. When I poured water into my dehydrated system it made me feel tipsy all over again. I had a shocking headache and almost no vision. Consecutive thought was quite impossible. I knew that something pretty shattering had happened, but I couldn't pinpoint it. It wasn't until the late afternoon that, feeling frail as parchment, I began at last to get the conversation with Skaliga into focus.

Several things had emerged from that squalid encounter, and I didn't like any of them.

First, it was no longer possible to believe that Stefan Raczinski had been the victim of mistaken identity. Unlike Lutkin, Skaliga had described his characteristics so exactly that I couldn't doubt it was Marya's father he'd been talking about.

That still left the alternative that the charge against Raczinski had been deliberately concocted—that Lutkin and Skaliga had been briefed to give lying testimony at a bogus propaganda trial. But in that case, would Pavlov have gone to the trouble of producing Lutkin for me? Or, once produced, would he have been allowed to give such a pitiful exhibition of uncertainty about Raczinski? Wouldn't he have been well primed beforehand about the man's appearance? It seemed more than likely.

Then there was the matter of the wound in the knee. That was what worried me most of all. Skaliga had been utterly convincing about having seen it—all the more so because he'd been well under the influence when he'd told me. *In vino veritas. . . .* Besides, his description had been perfect. . . . Yet I had a clear recollection of Marya telling me that the wound had been received in guerrilla fighting after Raczinski's escape—and she could only have got that from her father. Had he lied to her? And if so, why?

There was only one explanation I could think of. His claim to have been a Polish patriot who'd miraculously survived the war in a series of Nazi camps would have been far less credible if he'd had to admit to an early leg wound. The Nazis had sent men to camps to work, not to convalesce. The ailing had been quickly dispatched. . . . But of course, if Raczinski had been an informer, that wouldn't have applied. . . .

My faith in him had been shaken. Now I couldn't help wondering about the rest of his story. . . .

I bathed and shaved, cutting myself only slightly, and around six-thirty I went downstairs in search of nourishment. Slattery and Logan were talking in the sitting room.

They both grinned when they saw me. Logan said, "My, you look a mess, Senator. . . . Did someone clobber you in Mali Pereulok?"

"That's what it feels like."

"Have a drink."

I shuddered. "Never touch the stuff. . . ." I lowered myself gently onto the settee. "Has anything happened that I ought to know about?"

"Not a thing," Slattery said.

"How's the foot, Cy?"

"I can limp about on it." He had it in plaster now. "There's a small bone broken—they say it'll take six weeks. Bloody nuisance."

"Never mind," Slattery said. "I'll be thinking of you all the time I'm away."

"That's mighty big of you, bud."

I said, "Have you fixed up with Schwartz, then, Joe?"

"Yes—we leave on Sunday."

"Flying?"

"No—there's no plane. . . . Train to Lvov, and then a branch line to a place called Slawno."

"Lvov . . . ?" I hadn't associated Lvov with the Carpathians, but now I remembered what Raczinski had said about it being close to the mountains. Suddenly a thought struck me. "Cy, have you still got your railway ticket?"

"Yes, I reckon so. . . . Why?"

"When's the reservation for?"

"Tomorrow night."

"I'd like to buy it."

He looked at me in surprise. "You going skiing too?"

"No—I want to go to Lvov. . . . There's something I want to look into there—rather badly."

"I don't get it, Senator. There's no prize with my ticket —you could have got one any time from Intourist. They run a hotel in Lvov. . . . Why the cloak and dagger?"

"I don't want anyone breathing down my neck. I want to browse around on my own."

"Pushing your luck a bit, aren't you?" Slattery said. "Getting sozzled in Mali Pereulok—then going off on a snooping trip. . . ! I hope your paper's paying you danger money."

"It's nothing to do with the paper, Joe—this is a personal matter. . . . I'd tell you about it—but it's kind of fluid."

"We're not curious," Cy said. "Not more than somewhat. . . . Where are you going to sleep in Lvov, though? You can't just bum around—not this weather."

"I'll probably get through all I want to do in one day. Then I'll go to Intourist and ask for a bed and a ticket back."

"Boy, will they be interested!"

"At that stage, it won't matter. . . . Look, will you blokes cover for me if the Nark rings up? Say I've got flu or something. I'll only be missing for a couple of days."

"What about Katya?"

"Oh—tell her I'm staying with someone from the Embassy."

Slattery nodded slowly. "Okay—we'll see to it. . . . But I hope you know what you're doing, Tim. . . . You could easily get slung out on your neck when they find out what you've been up to."

I shrugged. "There are worse fates," I said.

Twenty-four hours later I was on the train to Lvov. It was an overnight journey and if my mind hadn't been so full of doubts and anxieties I'd have enjoyed it. I had a comfortable berth in a "soft" car, the *provodnik* was attentive and brought glasses of tea whenever I wanted them, and the broad-gauge train ambled along soothingly at thirty miles an hour. I managed to catch up on some of the sleep I'd lost since my jag with Skaliga, and when we ran into Lvov at ten in the morning I felt physically ready for anything. I had no luggage except my pajamas and a toothbrush in a briefcase and I simply walked off the platform and that was that.

Despite the awkward revelations of Skaliga, I'd come to Lvov in hope. For all I knew, the discrepancy over the leg wound could have some perfectly innocent explanation. The actions of Pavlov, the vagueness of Lutkin, had to be considered against the tortuous background of Soviet Officialdom. Though my belief in Raczinski had been shaken, it certainly hadn't been destroyed. On the contrary, I now hoped to find evidence supporting his story—evidence, in particular, that he had been Polish-born, that he had been a citizen of Lvov, and not, as Skaliga had declared, a German. The odds were clearly against me after such a long time, especially as I lacked some basic information—where he'd lived with his wife, where Marya had been looked after during the war, and where her father had found her. But I did know that he'd worked at the University, and I knew where he'd been brought up as a boy—Biesczady Street. I even knew what the family house had looked like. So I'd quite a bit to go on.

I bought a guide to the town at a kiosk and quickly planned my route with the help of a street map. I'd travel on foot, I decided. A taxi would save time, but I'd be much more conspicuous. I'd go first to the University. From there I'd move on to the town hall, where the registry of births, deaths, and marriages was located. Finally, I'd call at Biesczady Street. I set off at a brisk pace. It was a splendid day for walking, with just enough frost to keep the light covering of snow crisp and dry. I soon realized why Raczinski had liked the town so much. It was beautifully situated in a circle of hills, with the snow-covered slopes of low mountains shining in the distance. Its streets and squares were clean and spacious, and there were parks and gardens everywhere. Fascinating tumuli were dotted about the town, surmounted by castles and monuments which at any other time I'd have liked to look at. There was a feeling of age and history about the place—of Polish history. A lot of the people I passed were talking Polish, and most of the rest Ukrainian. Momentarily, in spite of the official Russian presence, I could almost feel I'd left the Soviet Union.

I crossed the river Peltew, now frozen, where Raczinski had told me he'd fished as a boy, and made my way to the University via a street named Trzeciego and a public park which the guidebook informed me had once been called the Garden of the Jesuits. Inside the University building I quickly found the secretariat and introduced myself as a British correspondent on holiday from Moscow. I had been asked by a Polish friend, I said, to see if I could trace a man named Stefan Raczinski, who had been a student there just before the war. Could they help me? Had they any records of any sort? Was there anyone who might remember him?

They were interested, friendly—but regretful. They had no information of that kind at all, they said. The records of twenty-five years ago had all been lost or destroyed in the war. Almost everyone who had been there at the time of the invasion, students and teachers alike, had been killed in the fighting or worked to death in the camps. After the war, the University had had to make a completely fresh start. It was virtually a new institution.

I was disappointed—but not greatly surprised. I thanked the secretary and set off at once for the town hall. I found it in the market place, a vast square lined with some fine sixteenth-century houses, in one of which—a plaque announced—John Sobieski had lived. The registry office was busy and I had to queue for nearly half an hour before I got attention. When I finally reached the counter I told the same story I'd told at the University, except that now my interest was in the records of Stefan Raczinski's birth, of his marriage just before the war, of Marya Raczinski's birth, and of her mother's death. The clerk listened with increasing impatience, shaking his head and in the end interrupting me. No records had survived the war, he said. It was well known that the Germans had destroyed everything. Now, if I would forgive him, there were others waiting. . . .

I wasn't too despondent. I'd dispatched these necessary inquiries quite quickly and I'd still plenty of time for what I'd all along regarded as the best bet. I stopped at a café in the square for a glass of tea and a ham roll, checked with my map again, and walked through to Biesczady Street. As I turned into it, my spirits rose sharply. I could see at once that this was the street Raczinski had described. For a hundred yards along one side of it there was a garden that looked like a piece of natural country. Children were sliding and tobogganing down the slopes of attractively rounded hillocks. Through the gate I could see the one touch of formality that Raczinski had mentioned—the fountain. Not only that, but almost opposite the gate there was the white, three-storied house with the balconies, where he'd been brought up. Now let Skaliga say he was a German! With deep relief, I went into the house and knocked at the first door.

During the next hour I called at every flat in the building, asking particularly to speak to any middle-aged or elderly people who might be around. It must, I reckoned, be thirty years or more since Raczinski had lived and played here—but anyone over about forty might remember him, or the Raczinski family. It was an inquiry that needed a lot of luck—and in fact I didn't have any. The flats had changed hands over and over again, I was told. In the whole block, I failed to find even one long-term resident. It was the war, they all said. The war had changed everything. . . . Well, at least I'd seen the garden.

I had time on my hands, now, and I thought I might as well try the block next door. There, at the top of the building, I had an unexpected break. One of the rooms in one of the flats was occupied by a very old man—a Pole, but Russian-speaking—who had lived in the neighborhood for over fifty years and in that house for thirty. I told him of my search. I tried to describe what I thought Raczinski might have looked like as a boy. I said he'd probably had a big head and unusually high forehead, even then. I said he'd been an active boy—as though that marked him out from most others. A boy who used to play a great deal in the garden opposite. . . .

The old man gave me a puzzled look. "But, *gospodeen,*" he said, "there was no garden at that time. All this was a brickfield. It was not until just before the war that the garden was made. I should know, for I helped to make it. . . ."

III

I traveled back to Moscow in a mood of anger and dismay. My doubts about Raczinski were no longer balanced by a lingering personal trust. The moment had come, it seemed to me, when I had to face not only the possibility but the likelihood that Marya's father had done precisely what the Russians had said he'd done. Why else would he have invented a false background for himself? He must have been in Lvov at some time, I supposed, for his descriptions to be so accurate—but he certainly hadn't been brought up there. Possibly he'd passed through it during the war. Perhaps with the German army! He could have been serving when he'd got his wound. I didn't know. All I knew was that he'd lied to me, deliberately and brazenly—and that was enough. He'd gone out of his way to draw a nostalgic picture of a Polish past that he'd never had—and he'd hardly have done that if he hadn't had another, shameful past to hide.

Now that I'd come to suspect him, I began to see other aspects of his behavior in a more sinister light. The way he'd concealed the fact of the trial from Marya for all those years. He'd said he'd done it out of consideration for her and because the charge had caused him no concern—but the explanation could just as well have been guilt. . . . Also, the way he'd made no real effort to defend himself against the charge—preferring, perhaps, not to stir up any more trouble than he was already in. . . . Then there was his recent state of health, his anxiety illnesses. Could that be his past catching up with him? Remorse for the things he'd done, the things he'd seen, in those ghastly camps? Or fear—fear of retribution?

It seemed possible. Yet even now, in spite of his proved lies, in spite of the mounting evidence against him, I found it very hard to see Raczinski as a man with a despicable past—a creeping informer. My instinct had been to admire and like him. He'd appeared to me a man of caliber and principle and imagination—the very opposite of the mean and sordid type who'd deceive and betray helpless prisoners in a death camp. He'd seemed a kind, agreeable man—as well as a most affectionate father. Not that that meant anything. I couldn't forget that some of the worst criminals of Auschwitz had later become respectable married men, fond of their children, and reputed by neighbors to have hearts of gold. You just couldn't tell. . . .

I thought of Marya. Whatever her father had done, I couldn't believe that *she* knew. I had such a clear and vivid picture of her in the days of our happiness—fresh and innocent, altogether healthy, untroubledly gay. Yet the genes must be there. . . . Perhaps, I thought, in my growing desperation, she wasn't Raczinski's daughter at all. Apart from the fact that they both had green eyes, they weren't a bit alike. Perhaps he'd found her somewhere on his flight to the West and taken her along with him, hoping that the company of a child would help him to get into England. There must have been hundreds of orphaned, uncared-for babies on his route. . . .

I continued to mull over the facts and the theories all the way to Moscow—without reaching any conclusion. The only thing I knew for certain was that I'd never rest now until I'd established the truth—and that there was only one way to do it. The moment I reached Arbat I rang the Nark and asked for a meeting with Pavlov.

There were several letters on my desk upstairs. One of them was from Marya. It was in answer to the one I'd sent her a fortnight before. It read, in part:

I *have* been thinking about our situation, darling—

all the more since I got your letter, which made me feel very ashamed. I know now that I shouldn't have rushed off as I did, even though it was from the best of motives. It was stupid, as well as unfair, and I'm truly sorry.

As for our problem—well, what with your letter, and Daddy's persistent arguments, I'm almost persuaded that I was wrong about that, too. Everything depends, really, on *your* attitude—and you sound so certain and confident that I can't help feeling I may have got things out of proportion. Of course, it would be marvelous if you could topple the whole beastly case, and I'm longing to hear if anything more has happened. But—well, darling, I expect this will sound very feeble to you, after all the trouble I've caused, but if you still want me at Easter I'll probably be around, whatever happens. Absence is a very potent way of clearing the mind, and the truth is I love you so much I just can't face giving you up because of some remote contingency. . . .

I tossed the letter back on the desk. Forty-eight hours earlier it would have made me a deliriously happy man. Now the irony of it was almost more than I could bear.

Pavlov's manner, when we met, was distinctly cool at first. I guessed he'd had a report on me—and I was right. "I understand from Intourist," he said, "that you've been visiting Lvov."

"Yes."

"It's certainly one of the pleasantest of Russian cities. . . . Did you feel in need of a break?"

"No," I said. "I was making a few more inquiries about Stefan Raczinski."

"In Lvov? What took you there?"

"Raczinski told me he was born in Lvov and lived there as a boy."

"I see. . . . And this visit followed, I imagine, your unsettling talk with Pavel Alexandrovitch Skaliga."

I smiled grimly. "I thought we'd discovered all the mikes in Arbat. Obviously we hadn't."

"That, Lord Quainton, I take to be a joke. . . . What in fact happened was that Skaliga went to the authorities after he had sobered up and told them of the conversation he'd had with you. I think he was a little afraid that he'd talked out of turn—though of course he was at perfect liberty to say anything he wanted to. . . . If I'd thought for a moment he'd be such a useful witness, I'd have had him along instead of Lutkin. . . . So what did you discover in Lvov?"

"That Raczinski lied to me," I said. "He didn't live there when he said he did."

"No. . . ? Well, I can't say that surprises me very much. . . . But how did you manage to find out after all this time?"

I explained about the garden, at some length.

"Yes, I see. A rather bad oversight on his part. . . . So what are your feelings about him now, Lord Quainton? Do you still think he was not guilty of the crime for which he was sentenced?"

"I desperately want to," I said. "But after what Skaliga told me—and with this fresh evidence—I must say I find it very difficult."

Pavlov nodded. "My own view, after we saw Lutkin, was that the position was open—as you know. Now there seems to be no doubt whatever—and I'm sorry. The problem for you must be a very distressing one. . . . Have you any idea what you will do?"

"Yes," I said, "I'm going back to England. That's why I wanted to see you. I'd be glad if you could fix up my exit visa as soon as possible."

"I'll do that, of course, if you wish it. . . . Is this a temporary return you have in mind, or a permanent one?"

"Temporary, I would think."

"Your paper will make no difficulties?"

"At the moment, I hardly care. . . . I've got to get the truth from Raczinski, once and for all."

"You're going to confront him?"

"I am, indeed. I'm going to ask him why he lied, and where he *was* born. He may have a satisfactory explanation for everything. I hope he has. I'm not judging him—yet. But I must *know*."

Pavlov gave an understanding nod. "I can see that this business has upset you very much, Lord Quainton. In the circumstances, I feel you are wise to go, for nothing corrodes the mind like uncertainty. Once you've established Raczinski's guilt—as you surely will—your problem, in a way, will be simpler. I would say only this, at the risk of impertinence—that a daughter does not necessarily take after her father. . . . Good-bye, Lord Quainton. I will see that you have your exit visa within twenty-four hours."

I dropped in at Intourist on my way back from the Nark and ordered my air ticket to London. Then—not feeling like being quizzed by Cy and the others at the moment—I went and lunched alone at the Aragvi, a Caucasian restaurant in Gorki Street. I got back to Arbat just before five and retired to my room to pack a suitcase and mentally draft the service cable I'd send to the office before I left. There was no question of asking for permission and I finally decided on the simplest possible version—REGRET RETURNING FORTHWITH URGENT PERSONAL MATTER QUAINTON. Cole wouldn't be pleased, especially if I felt unable to explain what it was all about when I saw him, but I'd be paying my own fare and I might well be back in Moscow in a week, with nothing much lost from the paper's point of view.

The Americans didn't come in to dinner. I told Miles I was flying home for a few days and he said he wished he could. He knew by now that I was involved in some pretty serious personal trouble and he didn't ask any questions. We both pretended it was a normal thing to commute between Moscow and London, and discussed over dinner the implications of a new visit that Castro was about to pay to the Soviet Union.

At nine o'clock, the phone rang. It was Nina Alexandrovna calling me from the Nark. They worked all hours at that place.

"I rang to tell you, Lord Quainton, that your exit visa has come through."

"Good—thank you, Nina. I'll collect it in the morning."

"This evening, also, we received the authorization for your Ukraine trip. . . . Do you wish to cancel it?"

"Oh, lord. . . ! That *would* have to happen."

"Mr. Pavlov asked me to say that the trip is all arranged and that the itinerary is the one you suggested. We were waiting only for the authorization. . . . He wondered if perhaps you would prefer to make the trip first and then go to England."

I hesitated. "If I did, when would I leave?"

"According to the schedule, the day after tomorrow, in the morning. . . . Mr. Pavlov asked me to say that he does not wish to influence you in any way, but that it may not be easy to arrange the trip again this winter. A great deal of preparatory work has been done."

"Yes, I appreciate that. . . . Nina, I'll ring you back in ten minutes. All right?"

"Of course."

I hung up, and sat by the phone in gloomy thought. I knew what I *wanted* to do. I wanted to see Raczinski and have it out with him, quickly. I wanted to get things straightened out with Marya, one way or the other. For the moment I'd lost all interest in the damned trip. Yet I didn't see how I could pass it up. Cole would never forgive me if he got to hear that I'd done so—and I wouldn't blame him. After all, I was supposed to be a newspaperman. And the showdown with Raczinski could perfectly well keep for a few weeks. As for Marya, there was probably no future for us now anyway. . . . It seemed to me I had no real choice.

I phoned Nina, and said I'd go.

I was much too busy next day to think any more about Raczinski. The kind of expedition I was going on would be no picnic in midwinter and careful preparation was required. I'd done one trip before in December and in spite of the tactful compliment I'd paid Pavlov about the way he organized things I knew very well what could happen. Your plane could come down on the wrong airfield and stand all night in a snowy waste while you steadily froze at twenty below. The boiler of your train could ice up, or the train could get stuck in a drift. You could spend whole nights at isolated stations, waiting for connections that didn't come. You could skid off a road in a jeep and not be hauled out for ten hours. You could arrive late and tired at a destination and find that you weren't expected. You could run short of food, drink, and tobacco unless you kept a close eye on your own supplies. And you could be very, very cold.

I looked after the last point first. Slattery had a tremendous sheepskin *shuba,* the sort that night watchmen were sometimes issued, and as he wouldn't be needing it on a skiing holiday he offered to lend it to me. It had a huge collar that turned up well above the head, it was drawn in tightly at the waist and neck to keep the wind out, and it had a full skirt that almost swept the ground. It was so large that at night it would make the perfect blanket. That, with my own fur hat, a pair of fleece-lined gauntlet gloves, and, of course, *valinki,* should take care of the cold.

Then there was the question of supplies. Russian hospitality on trips was magnificent—but you often had to wait for it. Russians are like camels—they stoke up, and then keep going. I'm not—I've no endurance, and after about seventeen hours without food I get hungry. So I dug out the old kitbag I use on these occasions and stuffed it generously with a well-tried selection of food—rye bread, fat bacon, pressed caviar, and chocolate. I also put in a half liter of vodka, a filled water bottle, and a change or two of underclothes. I made sure I had my passport and press card, a torch, a book to read, a map of the Ukraine, a wallet of rubles and a fat notebook—and I was all set.

In the afternoon I went to the Nark and met the man who was to accompany me on the trip as guide and watchdog. His name was Andrei Korzhenko. He was a big, broad-faced Ukrainian of about forty—genial, but impressively tough. He spoke English, not very well but with enthusiasm. He could have been a Nark minion, but I thought he was more likely to be from security. He shook hands warmly and said it would be a pleasure to take me around.

He produced a map—a much better one than I had—and together we went over the projected route. The way things had been arranged by Pavlov, we would go first to one or two collective farms in the heart of the Ukrainian steppe, because the weather was growing severer each day and the sooner we were through the more exposed part of our travels the better. From the steppe region we would work back to Kiev, the Ukrainian seat of government, and get a line on the administrative problems of the area in winter. Then we'd continue down to the industrial Donetz basin and have talks with workers and managements at a variety of enterprises. We'd call at a place named Krivoi Rog, a uniquely productive iron ore mountain that had always intrigued me, and finish up at Odessa on the Black Sea, from where we'd fly home. It seemed to me an excellent itinerary, and I said so. Now that the start was close at hand, I was beginning to look forward to the trip.

Korzhenko checked with me that I had suitable clothing, told me with a grin that if I forgot everything else I should remember vodka, and arranged to meet me at the airport at ten o'clock next morning. Before I left, Pavlov came out of his office, asked me if everything was satisfactory, and wished me a good journey.

It seemed appropriate that a trip designed to test winter efficiency should start with a forced change of plan because of the weather. At eight in the morning Korzhenko rang me to say the report from the airfield we'd been going to fly to was very bad, and that we would have to go by train instead. The railhead would be a place called Glubni, about a hundred miles east of Kiev. I told him that that was perfectly all right with me—in winter I preferred surface travel. A car picked me up shortly after midday and by two o'clock we were trundling south in a train that was patently no crack express.

We had a compartment to ourselves and we conversed pretty solidly at first, exchanging personal details and getting to know something about each other. Korzhenko told me he was originally from Poltava, where his father had been a blacksmith. He had a wife in Moscow, and three children, and he showed me their photographs. He said he understood I was a lord and the son of a lord, and what did it feel like? I said it probably felt very much like being the son of a blacksmith. He was interested in my job, and I talked freely about it. I was interested in his, but he talked less freely about it. His geniality, I soon discovered, was spasmodic—he was given to long periods of rather morose silence. However, since we were going to spend more than a month together, that seemed much to be preferred to constant chatter.

The five-hundred-mile journey was like any other train journey, only slower. I read a little, and dozed a good deal in the warm compartment. At intervals, a rather slovenly-looking *provodnik* brought us tea. There was no restaurant car and we ate when we felt like it. Korzhenko had his supplies in a cloth-covered attaché case. His choice of food was similar to mine, except that he had a taste for pickled herring. He had brought vodka, too, but he drank sparingly. So did I. When the train stopped at stations, which was often, we climbed down into the snow and stretched our legs. At ten o'clock the *provodnik* made up our beds, and we turned in. I lay for a while, thinking about the questions I would raise at the collective farms, thinking a little about Marya and the mess we were in. Then I dropped off.

The morning brought no noticeable change in anything —apart from the weather, which had worsened. Snow was flaking down from a lowering sky and we had to have lights on in the compartment. The view through the windows was unvaried and uninteresting—mostly flat, and dismally gray, with stark patches of birch here and there but little else to break the monotony. Somewhere south of a town called Konotop we had a long holdup, and shortly after that a change of trains which Korzhenko hadn't told me about. It was nearly three in the afternoon when we finally reached Glubni.

There, it soon became apparent that our enforced change of plan had not been adequately reported from Moscow. Whoever was supposed to meet us at the station hadn't turned up. Korzhenko went off to telephone and was away quite a while. Not for the first time, I could see distinct advantages in the Russian preference for conducted trips. All I had to do was exercise patience and tag along. The problems and anxieties were going to be Korzhenko's.

He didn't look particularly anxious when he returned —just very hot. "I am afraid there has been some misunderstanding," he said. "Tonight we will have to stay in Glubni. However, there is no need to worry—a car is coming and we will soon find a hotel. In the meantime, let us drink some tea."

We went into the station buffet, which was filthy, and drank tea out of dirty glasses, and talked about the Ukraine. After an hour a car arrived. There was a short sotto voce discussion between Korzhenko and the chauffeur, and we then drove through one of the drabbest provincial towns I had ever seen, to a miserable shack of a hotel which was reached by climbing a rickety flight of outside wooden stairs. Our welcome there was far from warm. The *hozyain,* a dark little rat of a man, said at first that he had no room for us. He got short shrift from Korzhenko, who seized him by the throat, shook him, and told him to make room—which he did. Later he produced some thin borsch and two plates of *kasha*—which at least was hot. As soon as we'd eaten, Korzhenko went off on another of his planning missions. He was in a better humor when he returned. "All is arranged," he said. "Tomorrow we go to Novi Gorod." It was near Novi Gorod that we'd be visiting our first collective farm. I said that was fine. Before we slept, Korzhenko wedged the back of a chair under the handle of the bedroom door. "This is not a good place," he said, as though he'd made a discovery. But the night proved uneventful—except for the bugs, which bit voraciously.

The morning dawned bright and clear, with a pale blue sky. My spirits rose—all the more when Korzhenko announced that there was no proper road to Novi Gorod and that we were going by sledge. A sledge journey was something I'd always hankered after, but had never managed to achieve. "Sixty-three kilometers," he said. "Four hours. And the perfect day for it. We start at nine."

Surprisingly, we did. The two-horse vehicle, driven by a peasant *izvostchik,* was waiting outside the hotel at five minutes to nine. The driver was an old man of ravaged appearance, with zigzag ears and a nibbled nose where the frost had got at him. The sledge was broad and stoutly made of wood and iron, with heavy metal runners —a relic of a passing age. We tucked ourselves well in under a thick skin rug, our *valinki* wedged against our luggage, our collars up and earflaps down. The *izvostchik* shouted something to the horses that sounded like *Hotyar!* and we were off.

It was a bumpy ride over the uneven snow of the town, but as soon as we emerged into the open plain the motion became smooth and comfortable. Except for the hiss of the runners and the muffled sound of the horses' hoofs, our passage was noiseless. The steppe, in the early morning light, looked breathtakingly beautiful. The snow, clean and sparkling, lay in narrow wind-blown ridges, like the ridges of sand on a seashore. They were yellow on one side in the sunlight, purple on the other in the shadow, giving a lovely "shot" effect. The still air glittered with myriads of ice crystals that pleasantly pricked our faces. I had rarely felt so exhilarated.

There was, as Korzhenko had said, no proper road through the white expanse, and in places even the track was almost obliterated by recent snow. But the horses seemed to know their way, and the *izvostchik* did little to guide them. Just occasionally, when the plain dipped into unexpected little ravines that had to be climbed out of, he gave that extraordinary shout *Hotyar!* and a touch of the whip to encourage them. But mainly the ground was as level as a table top. It was also empty—the emptiest land I'd ever seen. There wasn't a tree, a building, or a living soul to be seen in any direction. *"Prostor!"* Korzhenko said, with a great sweep of his arm. It was the word the Russians use to describe the limitless space of their country. Korzhenko sounded as proud as though he'd personally created it.

We'd been going for nearly two hours when I caught a whiff of wood smoke on the dry air. A mile further on we came to a tiny settlement—a typical steppe settlement, Korzhenko said. Its color-washed houses, built of baked earth, had rounded, igloolike roofs, and floors sunk several feet into the ground, so that as we passed by we could see right into the rooms. Korzhenko called a halt at one of the houses and with the briefest exchange of words organized glasses of hot tea from a peasant's samovar—while our *izvostchik,* his beard and eyebrows white with hoarfrost so that he looked more than ever like a patriarch, fed and watered his horses. Then we were away again.

The first thrill of the journey had now passed and the

second half was a bit wearing. A wind had got up—faint, but sharp as a razor cut. Soon my eyes began to run, and the tears froze on my cheeks. I could feel the hairs in my shrinking nostrils stiff with ice. My toes, however much I wriggled them in the spacious air pockets of the felt *valinki,* were slowly growing numb. So were my gloved hands. Korzhenko pulled his coat collar closer round his ears and agreed that it was cold. *"Holodno!"* he kept saying. *"Ochen holodno!"* We watched each other's faces for any sign of the white, bloodless patch that would require instant treatment with snow to restore the circulation. But we got through without suffering anything worse than discomfort. By one o'clock we had bypassed the little town of Novi Gorod and were driving under a tatty wooden arch with a red banner nailed to it extolling the virtues of collective labor, and the words "Kolkhoz named after Lenin" on a board beside it.

That afternoon, with introductions over and a substantial buffet luncheon out of the way, I got down to work with the Chairman, the Vice-Chairman, and the heads of the various farm sections. I explained that I wasn't concerned with the organization of the collective, but with how their members occupied themselves in winter and coped with their winter problems. We started off with some lively chat about their extreme conditions, on which they dwelt with a certain grim pride. They told me stories of the thermometer dropping to forty below, of careless fingers skinned at the touch of metal, of warning flags flying when it was too dangerous for children to go to school. Then we got down to real business. I produced my list of questions, which dealt with things like crop storage, machine maintenance, fuel supplies, and transportation, and we had a conference that lasted nearly four hours. They were interested in the subject and completely frank in their replies, and because nothing had to be interpreted we covered a lot of ground. They told me about winter arrangements for feeding and tending the animals; about their constant battle to build up adequate stocks of wood in an area that was largely treeless; about delayed coal deliveries and the struggle to maintain communications. They admitted there was some spoilage of crops, and told me of a big potato loss when the heating of a freight train had broken down. They told me about lectures and films they'd organized in some of the villages; about handicraft industries they were trying to encourage for the long winter days; about a special drive they were making to repair the low wooden carts on which they mainly relied for summer transportation. They discussed, with worried earnestness, the problem of keeping the peasants on the land at all in winter, when the attractions of the local towns were so much greater. They had figures on everything—comparative figures going back for years. If statistics could have made a prosperous economy, theirs would have been booming. As it was, I had the impression they were only just getting by. They were most agreeable people, friendly, vigorous, and eager, and I warmed to them. It wasn't their fault, nor the fault of men like them, that collectivization had been such a flop. The theorists had had a bad idea—an idea which simply didn't chime with human nature. These men were the struggling operators.

Korzhenko, who had soon tired of the discussion and had quietly disappeared, returned in the evening in good time for a tremendous banquet, which was attended by various Party and civic officials from the district as well as all the people I'd talked to. It followed the classic pattern on these occasions—fantastic quantities of food, vodka flowing like water, wine from the Caucasus, and endless speeches and toasts. I made my contribution, though I can't now remember what I said. At any rate, a good time was had by all, and those who were still capable of it got themselves up to bed soon after midnight.

Next day I was taken on a tour of inspection of the collective's broad estates, in a lorry that had to have a fire lit underneath it before it would start. I was shown potato clamps and grain stores, cowsheds and piggeries, a repair shop for tractors, and a dozen other things. I got back late and was given another enormous meal. Then Korzhenko, who had been doing some more telephoning, took over again. Shortly after ten, with farewells that bordered on the emotional, we set off in a *kolkhoz* car for our next railhead, twenty miles away. We reached it without incident, and the car left us there.

It was a remarkable station. It consisted of a small wooden waiting room, beside a single track, set down in an empty desert of steppe as flat as a frozen sea. More remarkable still was the fact that the waiting room was packed with men, women, children, and bundles—peasant families on the move. Heaven alone knew where they'd come from or how they'd got there. It was a pretty squalid scene and the stench was awful. But it was the only warm place for miles around, and Korzhenko and I squeezed in with the rest and sat down on the floor to wait. As usual, Korzhenko hadn't taken me into his confidence about our immediate plans, and I had to press him hard before I discovered that the train should arrive around midnight. In fact, we waited all night. Once, there was a false alarm, and everyone stirred, but mostly we just sat there beside our luggage, dozing. When I did go out for a breath of air, I found the night bitter. The sky was clear and starlit, the frost intense. On the whole, it was better inside.

Dawn came, but the train didn't. By now I was getting very tired of the place—but that dawn was a spectacle I wouldn't have missed. The sun came up above the firm line of the horizon as a clear red ball. A silver crescent of moon faded in the west. Then, in a matter of seconds, the expanse of virgin snow around me turned a deep scarlet. It was like standing in the center of a lake of icy fire. I enthused to Korzhenko, but he only grunted. I gathered later that he considered it a portent of bad weather.

The train arrived at nine o'clock. There must have been some bad breakdown, but I never heard what had happened. Personally I was too glad to be on the move again to ask questions. Our destination was a station called Krasnaya Tserkov, three hours away. There were no more holdups, but of course we were so late getting there after the night's delay that all Korzhenko's careful arrangements had been upset, and once more he had to start telephoning. I nibbled some chocolate and took a look around. The station wasn't quite as isolated as the one we'd left. Outside, there was a road of sorts, and away in the distance I could see the dome of a church. Near the station entrance, three peasant women with baskets had set up a small informal market. I admired their hardiness. As Korzhenko had prophesied, the weather was deteriorating. The sky had clouded, and a raw wind had begun to blow. It wasn't much of a day for sitting around.

I went back into the waiting room—which happily had emptied with the arrival and departure of our train. After half an hour or so, Korzhenko rejoined me. He said we'd have to wait for a car, but he wasn't sure how long. We waited all afternoon. People came and went. So did one or two more trains. Dusk fell, and we were still waiting. The transportation arrived at six—a decrepit station wagon with a visibly reluctant chauffeur. He said it was going to be a bad night for a drive, and couldn't we put up somewhere till morning? I thought it was a good idea, but Korzhenko, way behind with his schedule, was anxious to get through to the next *kolkhoz*. So we went.

We traveled over a "corduroy" road—a narrow strip of pine logs laid crosswise on the bare ground. It had a treacherous coating of snow and ice and an intolerably bumpy surface that sent us bounding to the roof every few seconds. A moaning wind blew horribly through drafty doors and windows. Presently it began to snow. It wasn't the soft snow we'd had before, but a dry, whirling powder that obscured the view. At first the fall was light, but as the wind strengthened, drifts began to form on the corduroy. I could hear the chauffeur grumbling to Korzhenko in the front of the car. He was saying that he couldn't see the road properly and that if we ran off it we could easily get stuck in a drift. He kept on muttering, and saying that we ought to turn while we could and drive back to Krasnaya Tserkov in our tracks. But Korzhenko wouldn't hear of it. We'd been going for more than an hour, he said, and must be nearly halfway to our destination. Besides, our tracks would be already covered—going back would be as difficult as going on. So we fought our way on, skidding and sliding, and the snow got worse. The drifts were getting deeper; visibility was negligible. Only the bumps told us we were still on the road. Suddenly the wipers packed up. I had a brief glimpse of a copse of birch trees on the left before the windscreen grew opaque. Then the car lurched, shot off the corduroy, and buried itself to the axles in a drift. One look at it from the outside told us there was no hope of getting it out on our own.

It was the chauffeur, peering through the flying powder, who spotted the pipe—a concrete pipe, nearly three feet in diameter, lying on the surface of the ground at right angles to the road. Beyond it we discovered another one, not joined—and another. Evidently some major constructional work was under way. Korzhenko, telling us to wait, set off through the copse with a torch, following the line of pipes. We waited, backs to the wind, stamping our feet. We both knew the position was pretty grim. At the best, it seemed, we should have to spend a freezing night in the car—and the way the storm was developing, we might well be buried by morning. . . . Then Korzhenko emerged from the wood. "It's all right," he called cheerfully, "there's a building. . . . Bring your things."

We needed no second bidding. I lugged my kitbag out of the car, and Korzhenko took his case, and we set off in the tracks he'd made, with the chauffeur following close behind. The pipes ran on, through the little wood and out into the open again. Ahead, I could see the loom of the building. It proved to be a single large room built of sectional concrete slabs—put up, I guessed, for the convenience of the workers on the pipe job. Beyond it was a wooden latrine hut. The building was locked and there was no sign of life. Korzhenko put his shoulder to the door and at the second heave the lock broke. We went in, flashing our torches. The room had two long rows of trestle tables, with wooden chairs for about forty men. Off it there was a little annex—a kitchen. Naked electric light bulbs dangled from the ceiling. Korzhenko clicked a switch, but nothing happened. He nosed around the kitchen, found the main switch and threw it. Still nothing happened. He looked in the box beside it and grunted. "It's the fuse," he said. We searched around for wire. After a moment the chauffeur pulled a rusty piece from an old crate. Korzhenko looked at it dubiously, shrugged, and tried it. The room blazed with light.

He grinned at me. "We're in luck," he said. "Allow me to welcome you to the best hotel for miles."

We were, indeed, in luck. Not only had we shelter and light, but there was a big stove in the center of the room and sufficient wood stored beside it to keep us in fuel throughout the night. There was no water supply—a row of birchwood buckets hanging in the kitchen suggested some outside source—but we had plenty of snow to melt. There was no telephone, which meant we wouldn't be able to ring for help in the morning—and as operations at the site seemed to have been suspended for the winter, there'd be no workers to call on. However, that problem could be dealt with when the time came.

The chauffeur, quite amiable now, chopped some kindling and lit the stove. When it was blazing merrily we all had a shot of vodka and a *zakuska* of bread and garlic sausage from Korzhenko's supplies—followed a little later by a more substantial meal and quarts of hot tea. The room, with its double windows, warmed up rapidly. The place was cleaner, and a lot more comfortable, than the hotel at Glubni had been. Our satisfaction grew as the blizzard outside became audibly worse. We had had a close shave.

Before settling down for the night I put on my outdoor things and paid a visit to the lavatory hut. The shock of the cold outside made me gasp; in that swirling white world, clothes seemed a feeble shield. The room lights threw a helpful glow around and I had little difficulty in negotiating the path, which had been blown clear of snow for most of the way by some trick of the wind round the building. All the same, those thirty yards were no fun. Neither were the primitive facilities of the hut. But at least it offered some cover.

When I opened the door to leave, I saw with dismay that the building was in darkness again. The rusty fuse must have failed. I shone my torch ahead, but it proved a hindrance rather than a help—the beam showed nothing but an opaque curtain of driving snow. I shone it down on the ground, thinking I'd retrace my own steps. Near the hut, where the snow had piled up a little, that was easy—but after a yard or two I could see no marks at all. My flat-bottomed *valinki* had left only the faintest traces, and the whirling powder snow had already obscured them. I stood for a moment in the slashing wind, trying to remember where the building had been in relation to the hut. A little to the left, I thought. I peered ahead, but could see absolutely nothing. I groped my way forward. A bit more to the left, perhaps? I took another half dozen steps—and plunged into a drift. By the time I'd got myself out of it, I'd lost my bearings altogether. Where the hell was I?

I stood and shouted. A faint shout came back—but in that howling blizzard it was hard to judge its direction. I tried again—and still I didn't know which way to turn. Then I remembered that on my way to the hut I'd had the snow at my back—so now if I faced it I ought to reach the building. I plodded on for twenty paces. I knew I was off beam because of the depth of snow, but I didn't think the building could be far away. I shouted again, with the full power of my lungs. This time there was no response at all.

I had no illusions now about the danger I was in. The building was a mere speck in the vastness of the steppe and the chance that I would stumble across it by accident was negligible. But if I didn't find it and had to spend the night in the open, I'd almost certainly perish. I fought down my rising panic and tried to consider the situation calmly. The building, I told myself, *must* be near. Any moment now, Korzhenko would get the fuse fixed and the light would come on. I'd see the glow, and I'd be all right. But in the meantime I couldn't just stand still or I'd freeze in my tracks. The best course seemed to be to walk in a tight circle and watch for the light.

I stumbled on, bearing always a little to the left. The wind was still rising, the curtain of snow becoming denser. The sharp crystals whipped painfully against my face. Breathing was difficult. Every few yards I fell into a drift. Slowly, I began to tire—and worse, to lose heart. By now the room light must surely be on again. I was too far away to see it, that was all. Mechanically, I plodded on. I knew I was hopelessly lost—but to stop was to die. While I kept moving, there was still a chance.

I don't know how long I kept going. I know only that I was near to exhaustion when I suddenly blundered into something hard. I shone my torch down. It was one of the concrete pipes. At once, hope surged through me. If I followed the line of the pipes, I must surely reach either the building or the car. In either case, I'd be safe. I struggled on with new vigor. But I'd reckoned without the drifts. They were so deep now that in places the pipes were buried and I was in danger of losing them. Time and again I sank to my armpits in the soft snow. Every step was a battle. I'd never make it. . . .

There seemed only one hope. I chose a pipe that was blocked with snow at one end and almost blocked at the other, and crawled in as far as I could go. The relief was indescribable. Out of the driving blizzard, and glowing from my exertions, I felt almost comfortable again. There was no draft in the pipe, no moving air at all. In a little while, I thought, the storm might abate, the snow stop falling. Then I'd be able to see the lights of the building. I tied my earflaps under my chin, pulled the high collar of my *shuba* round my head, drew my feet up under its skirts, and lay down.

I shall never forget that night—that long, long night. The storm didn't slacken. Slowly, the cold crept through me. I stirred often, changing my position, working my toes, my legs, my arms, in the narrow circumference of the pipe. I crawled up and down repeatedly on my hands and knees, trying to keep the circulation going. I found a slab of chocolate in my pocket and munched a piece at carefully timed intervals. Repeatedly, I looked at my watch. The hours dragged as no hours had ever dragged before. Finally I became so cold and wretched that I hardly cared what happened. Toward morning I dozed from sheer exhaustion.

I was aroused by voices. I was so cramped and stiff that I could hardly move. I raised my head painfully from the concrete and looked along the pipe. Through the gap in the snow I could see that dawn was breaking. Dawn—and I'd lived to see it! I crawled toward the entrance. It had stopped snowing and the wind had dropped. Everything was very still. The air seemed much milder. I looked out. The building was scarcely more than a stone's throw away! Korzhenko and the chauffeur were standing in front of it, gazing around. They seemed curiously unperturbed. I was on the point of scrambling out and angrily demanding why they weren't searching for me when I heard words that froze me more than the night had done.

"He's dead, all right. . . ." It was the chauffeur's voice, clear in the still air. "No one could have survived such a night."

"I shouldn't think so," Korzhenko replied. "We'll have

to find him, though. My instructions were to take his body back to Moscow."

"We'll find him after breakfast—he can't be far away. . . . It worked well, Andrei Andreivitch. . . . The perfect accident. . . ."

IV

They went back inside—and I just sat there, rigid with horror and disbelief. It didn't seem possible that I'd actually heard those words said. That they'd meant *me*. Such things simply didn't happen—not to correspondents. Not to conducted guests on a trip. It was an enormity. I must have misheard. . . . Yet I knew very well I hadn't. It wasn't just the words. I could see, now, how everything else fitted. The way that light had gone out at the crucial moment. And stayed out. The way no real effort had been made to look for me. One feeble shout, that was all. . . . I couldn't begin to imagine what had led the Russians to this step—but it was as plain as the snow around me that from the start of the trip they'd meant to kill me. *My instructions were to take his body back.* . . . Korzhenko had been given his orders in Moscow—and he'd simply been waiting for the right moment. In the blizzard he'd found it—and if it hadn't been for the pipe, I'd be dead.

Now what was I going to do?

One thing was certain—indignation wasn't going to help me. I stifled my anger and tried to consider the alternative courses of action coolly and realistically. One possibility was to walk back into the building and pretend I'd heard nothing—tell my story of the night's hardships and simply carry on. It had its attractions. At least I'd be able to thaw out, and eat, and gather my strength. No doubt Korzhenko would try to stage another accident later on, but now that I was on my guard he wouldn't find it so easy. And at some point, perhaps, I could give him the slip—get a train back to Moscow, seek the protection of the Embassy. . . . Going back into that room now would be like putting my head into the lion's mouth a second time, and I didn't fancy it—but wasn't it the least of all the risks?

I thought about it a bit more—and I realized it wouldn't work. They'd want to know where I'd spent the night—and I'd have to tell them I'd sheltered in the pipe, because when I left it my footmarks would give me away. It was so near the building that they'd have to assume I'd overheard their conversation. And that would force their hand. To be safe, they'd have to stage the next "accident" at once. I'd be better off trying for a getaway—however great the odds against me.

I'd no illusions about the odds. I was warmly clothed, but I hadn't a scrap of food with me. I'd a torch, passport, and money, but no map. I must be nearly thirty miles from the only railhead I knew of, in empty, almost roadless country that offered no cover apart from the drifts. And pursuit, once begun, would be relentless. If I got back to Moscow, I could make appalling trouble. They simply couldn't afford to let up now till they'd silenced me.

How long a start could I count on? Not, I thought, more than an hour or two. They might waste a little time at first, searching for my body—but they'd soon pick up the tracks I was bound to make on leaving. They'd know I'd survived, and they'd know which way I'd gone. There were only two things in my favor—they hadn't a telephone and their car was in a drift. But neither circumstance would hold good for long. If I intended to go, the sooner I got started the better.

At once, I faced a new problem. The moment I left the pipe I'd be visible from the windows of the building. I peered out, cautiously. I could see Korzhenko's head, his face. He was talking to the chauffeur. He wasn't looking in my direction. But any movement in the snow would be bound to attract his attention. It was too big a risk. I'd have to wait until they went off on their search—and hope they'd start at the back of the building, which was where

I'd disappeared. Reluctantly, I drew back into the pipe. . . . Then I suddenly had an idea. Maybe there was an escape route after all. I crawled through the pipe to the blocked end. The snow was soft—a thaw seemed to have started. I began to claw at it with my gloved hand, scooping it past me and pushing it back into the pipe. In a few minutes I had made a tunnel through to the next pipe. I crawled along it, and repeated the process, still under cover, and went through into the one beyond. I kept going. Several times along the route I had to clear more barriers of snow, but the pipes had been set down only a yard or so apart and I had no great difficulty. In fifteen minutes I was at the end of the pipe line and well out of sight of the building. I'd left a trail, because in places the surface snow had collapsed where I'd excavated between the pipes. Korzhenko was bound to realize what had happened when he started to look around. But it might not be for some time. With a feeling of achievement I scrambled out under the trees, shook the wet snow from my clothes and walked over to the station wagon.

The overnight drift was beginning to recede from its axles. I hadn't a hope of digging it out myself, but I didn't think it would take Korzhenko and the chauffeur long to get it on the road again. I opened the hood and took out the distributor arm. That should immobilize it indefinitely. I glanced in the trunk, in case there was anything I might find useful on my way, but it was empty except for the spare wheel and a can of petrol. I looked in the compartment under the instrument board. There, I found treasure—a lump of salami and a hunk of black bread. I stuffed them into a pocket and stepped out into the road. The wheel marks the car had made the night before were no more than shallow depressions now, and the snow didn't look impassable on foot. Momentarily, I debated which way to go. Back toward the distant railhead at Krasnaya Tserkov that I knew about—or on into the unknown? The known seemed preferable. With my back to the morning sun, I started to walk.

The snow covering was far from uniform. Where the road ran absolutely straight and level it lay only a few inches deep and I plowed through it without difficulty. At bends, or shallow dips, there were often drifts that I had to wade through. Mostly they lasted for only a yard or two, but in places I'd have lost the road altogether if it hadn't been for a line of tall guiding poles that marched beside it to the horizon. In other places the thaw had already gone so far that the logs of the corduroy were visible. I hadn't appreciated till now how far south I was, and what warmth there was in the winter sun. I would gladly have dispensed with my huge *shuba*—and *valinki* were no longer the ideal footwear. They didn't leak, but they grew soggy and heavy, slowing me down.

The road would have been a dreary one at the best of times. There was no variety, apart from the depth of snow—nothing of significance to catch the eye. No trees, no fences, no habitations, no animals, no birds—no sign of life at all. Once I thought I detected an indentation that could have been a track, running off to the left, but if it led to a settlement the place was hidden by the curve of the earth. Never had I felt so utterly alone as I did on that silent, featureless plain. I tried, as far as possible, not to think about my situation, for thought could bring no comfort. I was too tired in body and mind to try to work out why this disaster should have happened to me. Anger against Korzhenko and his bosses seemed a waste of energy. All that mattered for the moment was the distance I could put behind me and the distance still to go.

I was far from giving up hope of survival, but the outlook didn't improve as the hours passed. By nightfall, I reckoned, I would have covered little more than fifteen miles at my present rate of progress. Even if I kept going all night—which I'd have to do unless I was prepared to lie down in the snow—I'd still be some distance from Krasnaya Tserkov by morning. And by morning the hunt would surely have started. . . . However, there was nothing I could do about it, except plod on.

My one stroke of luck had been the finding of the salami. There was a whole loop of it, and I gnawed and chewed with relish as I plugged along. That, with the bread, and snow for water, gave me the strength to keep going. Another thing that heartened me as the day wore on was that I seemed to be walking out of the blizzard belt. The storm must have been a fairly local one, for by two o'clock my path was only occasionally blocked by drifts. I began to make much better speed.

It was shortly before three o'clock when I caught the sound of a distant engine. At first I thought it must be an airplane, for I could see no vehicle in any direction. Then, gazing back uneasily over the road I'd traveled, I made out a moving dot that could only be a car. It was at least a mile away, and coming on slowly—but in minutes it would catch me up. I felt sure it must be Korzhenko and the chauffeur—though I couldn't imagine how they'd got over the distributor problem. If it was, I was sunk. There wasn't enough cover on the steppe to hide a field mouse—and anyway they'd have seen me by now. I stopped and waited, my heart pounding. Then, as it came nearer, I relaxed. It wasn't the station wagon—and there was only one man in it. I still had a chance. Perhaps a better chance than before. As I watched it, it skidded to a halt in the snow. The man got out with a shovel and dug vigorously for a few moments. Then the car came on again, bumping and sliding. It had chains on its wheels—I could hear their distinctive whirring. It drew level with me, and pulled up with a jerk. The driver was a young fellow of about my own age, with a flat, peasant's face and a broad, concave nose. He wore the gray-green quilted jacket and quilted trousers of the countryside, and an incredibly ancient fur hat.

He stuck his head out of the window, staring at me. His expression was disbelieving—and with good reason. People didn't normally hike across the steppe in winter

—and after all I'd gone through I must have looked a sight.

"What on earth are you doing out here, *tovarisch?*" he said.

"My car got stuck in a drift," I told him. "Last night. . . ." I pointed back along the road.

"Ah. . . . So that was *your* car, was it? Twenty kilometers back. . . . You'd have done better to stay with it—there's nothing this way at all." He spoke with a strong country accent and a sprinkling of Ukrainian words, and I had to listen carefully to understand what he said.

"I don't know these parts," I explained. "I was driving from Krasnaya Tserkov when I was overtaken by the storm. I spent a terrible night in the car—if the weather hadn't changed I'd have frozen. This morning, as the road was blocked, I thought I'd better walk back and try to get help. But it's farther than I remembered. . . . Where are you going to?"

"To Negoreloye. That's a village off the road, fifteen kilometers ahead. You'd better come with me."

"I'd be grateful. . . . Is there a telephone there?"

"No—but tomorrow I have to drive to Krasnaya Tserkov myself, and I will take you with me. It will be just as good as telephoning today. No one will come out to help you until tomorrow."

He opened the door and I climbed in, thankfully. As long as there wasn't a telephone, I'd go anywhere.

"You've probably saved my life, comrade," I said.

He grinned. "I wouldn't be surprised. This is a bad road—a very exposed road. I've been digging myself out all the way along."

I relaxed in my seat. The car was an ancient Moskvitch with poor springs—but to sit down was wonderful. "What is your name?" I asked.

"Scorbin," he said "Ivan Ivanovitch Scorbin. . . . And yours?"

I gave the first name that came into my head. "Pavlov," I said. "Alexei Alexeivitch."

He nodded, watching the snow on the road. "You're from the town?"

"From Moscow," I said. "I'm a journalist. On the staff of *Vechernaya Moskva.* I've been checking up on the winter wheat situation down here. . . ." It sounded an unlikely assignment for a reporter from a Moscow evening paper, but I didn't think he'd know much about newspapers.

"The winter wheat situation is bad, Alexei Alexeivitch—I can tell you that. The snow has come too late again—much of the grain is frozen. And after last summer's bad harvest—*oy yoy.* . . . They say wheat is coming into Odessa from Canada. I hope it is true. If not, there will be hunger before the spring."

"You work in a *kolkhoz?*"

"Yes—the Mikoyan, a few kilometers beyond Negoreloye. In the summer I am a tractor driver. In the winter, a mechanic. . . ."

He was a voluble man, and he continued to chat to me as we drove along. He didn't, it appeared, live in Negoreloye himself, but in a village nearer the *kolkhoz.* He was going to stay the night at Negoreloye in a comrade's house, and in the morning they were to drive together to what he called "a regional conference on spare parts" at Krasnaya Tserkov. "You must spend the night with us," he said.

"You're very kind, comrade."

He gave a realistic shrug. "What else could you do. . . ? You can tell us about Moscow, and what it is like to be a journalist. I have never met a journalist before."

"It will be a pleasure."

"They must pay you well for your work. . . . You have a fine, warm *shuba* there."

"Yes," I said.

At that point we ran into a light drift and I got out with the shovel and cleared the way. A mile or two farther on we turned off to the right along a narrow track. Soon the nature of the country began to change. The ground became more broken. Green copses dotted the plain, merging after a while into solid pine woods. When we came out into the open again there was a settlement ahead. It was the merest hamlet—no bigger than the one Korzhenko had stopped at in the sledge. But because there was timber near, its character was very different—it was more like the villages I'd seen in the north. It consisted of a couple of dozen *izbas* of rough pine logs, facing each other in two neat rows with an expanse of pressed snow between them for a street. Lights were already appearing in some of the windows. Ivan parked the car opposite the last hut on the right, and we got out.

"You're sure your friend won't mind?" I said.

"If he does," Ivan said with a grin, "he will cease to be my friend." He led the way into the *izba*. For the moment, at least, I'd found sanctuary.

I knew the name of the owner, for it had been written under the fretted eaves—Alexander Alexandrovitch Gretko. Ivan called him Sasha. He was a man about forty; broad, with a short, thick neck, and very fair, as so many Ukrainians are. Ivan introduced me, explaining my predicament, and Sasha welcomed me with a good handshake, his greeting neither too reticent nor too chummy. He apologized because his wife was not there also—it seemed she'd gone to spend the night with her sister at the other end of the village street. I suspected that the two men had been looking forward to an all-male evening, and the speed with which the vodka came out rather confirmed it.

I had never before had a chance to examine the inside of an *izba* and while Sasha prepared a *zakuska* and Ivan talked about the storm and the digging-out he'd had to do, I took a good look round. It was a single room, perhaps twenty feet square, with a curtained double door, tiny double windows, and bare log walls, their chinks sealed with moss and rags. In the daytime it must have been a dark place, but now an uncovered electric lamp blazed. The room, with its raised floor and wooden ceiling, was less spacious than I'd expected. It was also very warm, for the low, clay *pechka* in the center of the floor had a good fire burning in it. The air—what there was of it—smelt of smoke, cooking, and heavy, damp clothes. However, I was very happy to be breathing it. There was little furniture—a large brass bed, a couch, a homemade wooden table, a chair or two—and not much in the way of possessions. A few faded family photographs hung on a wall, around a large picture of Khrushchev. There was also a small icon with a candle in front of it. The Gretko family evidently believed in playing it both ways.

The warmth of the room and of Sasha's hospitality made me very sleepy after the arduous night and day I'd spent. I fought it by talking, as Ivan had wanted me to—giving a description of a newspaperman's life which certainly bore little resemblance to my own and was no doubt equally unlike a reporter's on *Vechernaya Moskva.* It seemed to go down very well, though, and the atmosphere became increasingly cordial. Presently Sasha prepared a meal, of proportions which I knew would denude the pantry for days. There were pickled cucumbers and tomatoes, fried potatoes and buckwheat *kasha,* sausage and cheese—with adequate, though not too much, vodka, and sweet tea to wash it all down. I did more than justice to the meal—and of course felt sleepier than ever when it was over. With some relief, I discovered that Ivan was also tired and ready for an early night. Sasha pressed me to take the brass bed, but I said I'd always wanted to sleep on a stove—which in the city I'd never had a chance to do—and begged to be allowed to. In the end I took the stove, now no more than comfortably warm; Ivan was given the bed, and Sasha had the couch. I spread my *shuba* over the stove, its collar humped for a pillow, and in moments I was dead to the world.

I woke as the first gray of morning showed at the window. I had had a long, dreamless night and felt in fine shape physically. Mentally was another matter. I lay there in the semi-darkness, thinking about my prospects.

Naturally, they hadn't improved while I'd been sleeping. By now, Korzhenko and the chauffeur must have discovered that I was alive and on the run. The snow marks and the immobilized car could have left them in no doubt about that. If they hadn't already managed to reach a telephone and start the hue and cry, they very soon would. The road was open again, and some vehicle was sure to pass that morning. I had to reckon that by midday, at the latest, my description would be out. It would be an unusual description, because of my big *shuba* and town suit, and I'd soon be picked up. All the more so because at midday I'd probably just be arriving in Ivan's car at Krasnaya Tserkov, which I'd gathered was no more than a large village, and where I'd stick out like a sore thumb.

The position, indeed, was only too clear. If I was to have any chance of getting back to Moscow safely, I had to reach Krasnaya Tserkov station without delay—and in different clothes.

I sat up cautiously and glanced across at Ivan and Sasha. They were asleep and motionless, their faces turned away from me. Ivan's quilted tunic and trousers lay over the back of a chair. He was shorter than me by an inch or two, but in girth he was about the same. I looked out of the window. The sky was dull, but no more snow had fallen. The car stood where Ivan had left it, in the empty street. I couldn't remember whether he'd taken the ignition key out. I tiptoed across to his clothes and felt in his pockets. After a moment, I found the key.

I still hesitated. If one of the sleepers woke and caught me in the act of swapping clothes, that would be it. But once I was away, they'd have neither transportation to pursue me nor telephone to report me—and I'd have gained hours. It seemed worth a try. With stealthy care, and a watchful eye on Ivan, I put on the trousers and tunic. The trouser legs were short, but when the bottoms were tucked into my *valinki* no one would know. I crept back to the stove and transferred my few belongings—money, passport, and torch—from *shuba* to tunic. For a moment I stood rooted, as Sasha sighed and stirred. But he seemed to doze off again. I pulled on my *valinki,* which had dried overnight, rammed Ivan's ancient hat on my head, and moved to the door. I had no qualms about taking his things for I was leaving him Slattery's *shuba* and my suit and it was more than a fair exchange.

Now I had to get out of the *izba.* This was the moment of greatest danger. Sasha was stirring again. Any second now he'd be opening his eyes. I lifted the door curtain a little and, as carefully as I could, tried to raise the iron latch. At first it wouldn't move. Then, as I pressed harder, it shot up with a loud metallic click. Sasha turned over toward me, awake.

I didn't bother about noise any more. I went quickly through the double doors and raced for the car. The street was still empty, the hamlet sleeping. I flung myself into the driving seat, thrust the ignition key into the lock, and pressed the starter. For seconds that seemed like an eternity it whirred without effect. Then the engine roared. I engaged a gear, shot back a yard, tried another, went forward, did a wide U-turn, and was off. The last thing I saw, through the mirror, was Sasha at the door of the *izba,* gesticulating in his underclothes. I don't suppose he'll ever forgive me for so abusing his wonderful hospitality—and I wouldn't blame him.

My spirits rose sharply as I left the hamlet behind. The car was running well. The petrol tank had nearly fifteen liters in it if the gauge was right—more than enough to get me to Krasnaya Tserkov. The mirror, when I swiveled it toward me, showed a face I hardly recognized under its two days' growth of beard. With my drab tunic and trousers, my battered *valinki* and my tatty hat, I wouldn't have much difficulty in passing for a Ukrainian *kolkhoznik*

—as long as I kept my mouth shut. If I had to talk, I could probably get by as a peasant from farther north. Things were looking up.

The track from the village to the highway had no confusing forks or turnings, and the car chains took care of the patches of soft snow. I reached the main road without mishap and swung right in the direction of Krasnaya Tserkov, driving now as fast as the bumpy corduroy would allow. I met two lorries and one car, but their drivers passed me without showing any interest. Nothing overtook me. After I'd covered about ten miles I raised the gilded dome of a church, ahead and a little to the left. That must be the one I'd seen from Krasnaya Tserkov station. Presently the road divided. There was no signpost, but the left-hand one obviously went to the village. I took the other one. There was no embankment to mark the line of the railway but presently I spotted a signal in the distance and then the building of the station itself.

I couldn't risk driving up to it in the car—that would be a sure way of attracting unwelcome attention to myself. I'd have to dump the car and walk. There was no place to hide it in the treeless steppe so I simply drove it off the road into a drift. I covered the remaining mile or so as fast as my *valinki* would carry me, slowing down only when I neared the station. There were people about—and I'd never known a genuine *kolkhoznik* to hurry.

Outside the waiting room, the market women were already setting out their wares. I was very conscious of having no luggage, not even a small bundle, and this seemed the moment to acquire some convincing impedimenta. With as little talk as possible, I bought bread, sausage, cheese, and mineral water, stuffing my pockets. I also bought a very large, solid cabbage, which I hoped would give me the authentic peasant touch. Clasping it tightly under my arm, I stumped into the waiting room. There were ten or a dozen people there, all country folk, dressed just about as scruffily as I was in quilted jackets and drab shawls and battered hats. They were sitting on the floor round the stove, in the usual patient attitudes. I wondered what train or trains they were waiting for. There was an inner office, but it was firmly shut and at the moment there was no sign of any official around.

I studied the faces about me, looking for a suitable person to question, and finally picked on an old peasant with bright, rather crafty eyes who was sitting a little apart from the others. He was a local man, it turned out, from Krasnaya Tserkov village. He said the next train was due at ten o'clock—it was now a little after nine—and that it would be going south. He, personally, was going to Odessa. He thought there would be a train for Moscow in the late afternoon—he had sometimes seen it pass—but he wasn't sure about the time. He asked me where I was from, and I said Tula. He looked at me a bit curiously, but he didn't ask any more questions.

I drifted away, disappointed and worried. It seemed more than likely that by the afternoon Authority would have descended on the station. With a man on the run in the district, the railway was an obvious escape route to close. Yet lightning speed was not a Russian characteristic—sputniks apart. I *might* be lucky—and Moscow was the only place where I'd be safe. . . . Maybe I should chance it. . . . In that case, I'd have to do something about getting a ticket—a problem which I'd had on my mind for some time. They weren't normally sold at stations—and they were always hard to come by. I knew very well what happened to travelers who boarded trains without them—they were put off at the next stop. For me, that could be a disaster. Perhaps, later in the day, when passengers gathered for the Moscow train, some official would appear and I'd be able to fix something on the quiet. At a pinch, I would have to try and bribe the *provodnik* on the train—but only as a last resort. People looking as I looked weren't usually in a position to bribe anyone. . . .

I went out on to the platform, away from potentially curious eyes. Ten o'clock came and went and there was still no sign of the Odessa train. It was actually signaled at ten forty-five, and it showed as a puff of smoke in the distance a quarter of an hour later. The people in the waiting room began to emerge. My uneasiness grew, for it seemed they were traveling south to a man. Soon I'd be left alone—conspicuously alone to the gaze of those market women outside. Maybe, I thought, I'd do better to leave the station for a while and come back nearer the time. The trouble was that I'd nowhere to go to—and aimless walking about might attract as much attention as sitting in the waiting room. Of course, there was still Ivan's car. . . . I glanced back along the road to where I'd ditched the Moskvitch. To my consternation I saw that a second car had pulled up beside it. Three men were inspecting its interior. The driver of the second car was trying to reverse out of the snow bank he'd got into. . . . It looked as though Authority was about to arrive.

I had to act fast—and I did. The Odessa train was steaming in. I rushed up to the old peasant I'd spoken to. "Sell me your ticket to Odessa," I said. "I'll give you fifty rubles." I showed him the money.

He gaped at me. His ticket had probably cost him ten. "I've *got* to get this train," I said—as though my urgency could possibly matter to him. "A *hundred* rubles. . . . You can always travel tomorrow."

He didn't speak—he just stared. Then, with a furtive glance to right and left, he closed his fist over the notes and gave me his ticket. I checked the number of the coach, which was seven; found it between numbers four and thirteen; showed the ticket to the *provodnik*, and climbed aboard.

The old man was still standing on the platform as the train left, gazing down at his riches. Authority—delayed by its encounter with the snow bank and now, belatedly, roaring up to the station—would no doubt question him about who had got on the train—and in the end he'd no doubt tell what had happened. But I didn't think he'd do it right away, because by selling his ticket for more than its face value he'd committed an offense. And he wouldn't want to lose that hundred rubles if he could help it.

The coach was a "hard" one, open from end to end and totally devoid of privacy or comfort. Its accommodation consisted of some twenty varnished wooden shelves in two tiers. At night each shelf would have been occupied by a single passenger, but now that it was daytime people had been allowed to crowd in and were sitting up on the lower shelves with their children, bundles, and animals around them. A few still lay stretched out on the top deck—their feet, bound in filthy rags, protruding into the passageway at nose level. The smell in the carriage was noisome, the heat stifling, the ventilation exiguous. The crying of babies, the clucking of hens, and the high-pitched chatter of the Ukrainian peasant women made the place a bedlam. I stuck it long enough to establish my right to a seat and then withdrew to a small unheated area near the outer door of the coach, set aside for heavy luggage. It was the through route to an indescribable lavatory, but I still preferred it to the Hogarthian scene inside.

There were frequent stops during the morning—and each one caused me anxiety. If Korzhenko's men had learned about me and phoned along the line, there could be a waiting posse and a search of the train at any one of them. But station after station passed without incident. People alighted, others came aboard. Passengers descended with kettles and jugs to get boiling water for their tea from the buffets and buy eggs and cucumbers from the squatting market women. Occasionally I descended too and strolled along the length of the train, keeping a wary eye open for any unusual knot of police or sign of special activity. But nothing happened.

Slowly, the day wore on. It was, I reckoned, some three hundred miles from Krasnaya Tserkov to Odessa, and at this rate we wouldn't be in till the next morning. Then, around three in the afternoon, the character of the train seemed to change. It began to go faster, and there were no more stops. The passengers had thinned out at a junction called Nova Ukrainka and the air in the coach had improved. I heard someone say there'd be no more stops before Odessa. It was the best news I'd heard that day. I sat down by a window and tried to think what I'd do when I got there.

Dusk fell, and dim yellow lights came on in the carriage. It was just possible to make out a neighbor's face—though the effort hardly seemed worthwhile. Presently the *provodnik* got a samovar going in his little cubby hole and I joined the queue for a glass of pale, sugarless tea. A man started to talk to me, asking me where I was from and what the weather was like in my part of the country. I answered him briefly, and as soon as I could I left him. Normally on a long journey I'd have been eager to talk, and hear things I could never learn in Moscow, but this was no moment to broaden the mind. I went back to my window seat and ate some bread and sausage and thought about Marya. She couldn't have seemed more remote if she'd been on another planet. I wondered if I'd ever see her again.

The first lights of Odessa's outer suburbs came into view shortly after nine o'clock. At once there was a stir in the carriage. People started to pack up their belongings and put on their outdoor clothes. The train went on, slowly now, clattering over points, switching tracks. We seemed to be running in. I clapped Ivan's hat on my head, picked up my cabbage, and moved toward the door. . . . Suddenly the train stopped with a jerk.

We stood for nearly half an hour, for no apparent reason; then crept on for a hundred yards and stopped again. The passengers began to grumble. The *provodnik* opened the coach door and stuck his head out. So did I. I could hear voices along the line. Men with torches were approaching. As they emerged from the darkness I saw that they had blue-topped, military-type caps. I knew then that my old peasant at Krasnaya Tserkov had been finally broken down. Unless I could leave the train, this looked like the end of the road.

I walked quickly back to my luggage compartment and peered through the windows of the exit doors, first on one side and then on the other. Blue-caps were already stationed beneath each of them. I tried the connecting door to the next coach and found it unlocked. I went through and on, edging past people, excusing myself, moving as fast as I could yet trying not to appear in a hurry. At each exit door I came to, there was a guard on the line. It looked as though the whole train was surrounded. I tried one more coach—a "soft" one—and hastily drew back. Two blue-caps were standing in the corridor, blocking the way. They were examining papers. In Russia everyone had to have papers—at the very least, an internal passport with a photograph. I turned and retraced my steps. Perhaps I'd be luckier in the front of the train. But as I re-entered my own coach I ran into more blue-caps. The search had evidently started at both ends of the train simultaneously. The male passengers were all queued up and a man with a shaved head and a fat neck was going slowly through their documents. A sharp voice called to me to get into line, and I did so. My brain felt numbed. It was like waiting for the tumbril, standing there. I wondered where the guillotine would be. . . .

The queue moved on. The light was so bad that Shaved Head was having to use a torch to see by. The time he spent on each passenger varied a good deal. The very old and the young were quickly dismissed. Two youths in front of me were passed through with only a perfunctory glance—and suddenly I was at the head of the queue.

The shaved man thrust out his hand. "*Dokumenti*, comrade." I loved that "comrade." He shone his torch at me and gave me a long, hard look. Already I thought I could read suspicion in his face. No doubt he was working to a description. I clapped my hand to the breast pocket of my tunic, as though feeling for my papers. I'd have to say

I'd lost them—not that it would gain me anything, except a short respite. Then I felt something stiff in the quilting. I eased the contents out. Documents. . . . Ivan's documents. . . . Well, I'd nothing to lose. In silence, I handed them over.

Shaved Head shone his torch on Ivan's passport, then again on me. "A poor likeness," he said.

I forced a grin, fingering my growth of beard. "One cleans oneself up for a photograph, comrade."

He looked me up and down. "You seem taller than 1 meter 68."

"Well, that's my height," I said. "In bare feet, of course. No doubt the *valinki* give me a few extra centimeters."

"Where do you work?"

"At the Kolkhoz Mikoyan, near Negoreloye. . . . I'm a mechanic in the winter, a tractor driver in the summer."

"What are you doing in Odessa?"

"I'm on *komandirovka,*" I said. "A conference on spare parts."

"Where are your travel papers?"

"I'm afraid I left them behind," I said. "A stupid thing to do—but I was in a hurry to catch the train."

He looked grim. "Where is your luggage?"

I jerked my thumb toward the luggage compartment.

"Get it," he said.

I shrugged, and walked through the coach to the luggage section and past it to the doors. The blue-caps were still on guard. I was so desperate now that, given half a chance, I'd have tried to make a break for it. But the nearest guard was standing less than ten feet away. He looked a hefty fellow and he had a gun holster at his side with the flap open. A little beyond him there was another guard. It was hopeless. I'd just have to go back and face the music. . . . Then, as I turned, I caught the rumble of an approaching train. I paused a moment. It came by slowly on the next track, blowing its whistle to clear the line. A goods train, drawing flatcars and trucks, mostly empty. . . . I opened the carriage door. The blue-cap was standing back to let the goods train pass. He glanced up as the door opened, shouted at me to close it, and snatched the gun from his holster. I could see an empty truck approaching. I had no weapon—except my cabbage. But that was enough. I hurled it at him. It caught him clean between the eyes and knocked him backward. The empty truck drew level—and I jumped.

I landed with a thud in the bottom, rolled over, and hit the side of the truck hard. The train rumbled on. Above the sound of the wheels I could hear a crescendo of shouting voices. For the moment, all was confusion. I caught the hiss and heat of the passenger locomotive as my truck went by. The goods train was drawing away. I crouched down in the darkness, praying that it would keep going, that it would put on speed. Instead, a hundred yards on, it clanked to a stop. Behind me, I could hear pounding feet. The whole pack was after me now—and the truck had become a trap. I jumped down, and raced away across the multiple tracks. Someone blew a blast on a whistle. A voice cried, "There he is!" I stumbled over a sleeper, recovered myself, and rushed on. The pursuit was close—but at least I wasn't hampered by a long military overcoat, as the blue-caps were. In a moment I came to an iron fence and turned along it, looking for a gap. Fifty yards on I found one. I shot through it, crossed some kind of yard, clambered over a low wall, and found myself in a dark, deserted street. I turned to the left, running now at full speed. I couldn't see any buildings. I could hear the blue-caps, still on my tail, shouting and blowing their whistles. Suddenly the street came to an end. Ahead was what looked like a stretch of waste ground. I stumbled on, fighting for breath, soaked in sweat. There was a lot of rubbish on the ground, that I kept tangling with. I knew I couldn't keep up the pace much longer. . . . Then, without warning, the earth seemed to give way beneath me. I felt myself slithering, falling. There was a blinding flash in my head—and I lost touch with the world.

V

I came round in pitch darkness. I was lying in a crumpled heap on a hard, cold surface. I'd no idea where I was or how long I'd been unconscious. My head ached, but my mind was clear. I remembered falling—and I remembered the chase. The chase! I lay listening. There wasn't a sound of any kind. Wherever I was, the hunt was somewhere else.

I moved my arms and legs and felt experimentally around my body. I was bruised and sore but I didn't seem to have broken any bones. I groped for my torch and clicked it on and swiveled the beam around. I could hardly believe what I saw. I was lying at the bottom of a narrow shaft—a slide, not quite perpendicular, of loose earth. To left and right, a tunnel stretched away into the darkness. It was five or six feet wide and a little over six feet high. Its roof was arched, its sides smooth and straight as though they'd been carefully worked. They were of a yellowish stone—some kind of sandstone. On the wall opposite me, someone had painted a slogan in rough black letters—"Death to the German Invader!"

I looked at my watch. The time was only ten thirty-five. I couldn't have been out for very long.

I peered up the shaft. It was so narrow and rough that it could hardly have been intended as an entrance when the tunnel was excavated. Through the opening at the top I could see one bright star. It was hard to judge how far away the surface was, but I didn't think I'd have any difficulty in climbing out when the time came.

I wondered how far the tunnel went, and set off to explore. After a few yards, it forked. I took the right-hand fork. Almost at once it divided again. The place was a labyrinth—and I lacked an Ariadne. I'd have to be careful. I went on, slowly, bearing always to the right. That way, I'd have no trouble getting back. The air was fresh, the tunnel remarkably dry. Its dimensions remained constant all the time. I guessed it had been hewn out to provide building material. I seemed to have read somewhere that Odessa was built of sandstone.

The way was strewn with relics of earlier occupation. There were rusty cans, battered cooking utensils, accumulations of dry wood, and the marks of fires. Pieces of old newspaper littered the floor. There were discarded weapons—a broken rifle, a bayonet, a knife with a snapped-off blade—and some items of torn military clothing. There were grizzlier relics, too—a skull, and several incomplete skeletons. There were signs that an illegal press had once been at work down here, for I found two crudely printed leaflets calling for sabotage of the Nazi occupiers. In places the walls were black with signatures and dates and slogans—not all of them as recent as the Hitler war. One fading but still legible inscription read "All Power to the Soviets!" and another "Death to the White Guard Butchers!" These catacombs must have been the hiding place of revolutionaries and fighters for generations. They were still used, it appeared, by the adventurous young of Odessa. In a small chamber I found paper bags, some crumbs of food, the cardboard ends of cigarettes, two partly used candles, and a comic book. I pocketed the candles before making my way back to the shaft.

There, with the torch switched off to save the battery, I sat down and considered my situation. It was far better than anything I'd dared to hope for an hour earlier. I was no longer in imminent danger of capture. I had, for the moment at any rate, a reasonably secure base—certainly a safer one than any I was likely to find up in the town. I had enough food for at least two days and a bottle of mineral water that had miraculously survived my two falls. I had quilted clothes to keep me warm. So why make any move? Above ground, the security squads would be combing the city for me. Whatever I decided to do next, I'd be wiser to wait till the heat was off. Anyway, I could do with a rest. . . . I got out my bread and cheese and sausage and settled down to a leisurely meal.

After I'd finished eating there was nothing to do in the darkness except think—and I started to think about Korzhenko. Ever since his attempt on my life, my mind had been fully occupied with the problem of survival. Now, a little wearily, I turned my thoughts to the reason for it all. *Why* had the Russians wanted to kill me? What had I done?

It must, I felt sure, be something to do with the Raczinski case because—apart from asking for a trip—that was the only thing I'd concerned myself with since my return to Moscow. And it *had* developed into a very sticky business. All the same, where had I so lethally offended. . . ? Of course, I'd broken a few unwritten rules by pumping the witness Skaliga on his own and going off secretly to snoop in Lvov. . . . But the only result had been to confirm what the Russians themselves had said. It just didn't make sense. . . .

Perhaps it would have made more sense if I hadn't been so worn out by the long, anxious day and the desperate chase at the end of it. As it was, I got nowhere. Very soon I abandoned the problem and thankfully drifted off to sleep.

Once again it was the onset of daylight that roused me—a pale streak of it, coming down the shaft. I got stiffly to my feet, crossed the heap of debris, and looked up. The tunnel was nearer the surface than I'd supposed—not more than ten or twelve feet. Through the hole I could see a ragged circle of clear sky. At least I wouldn't have to sit in darkness all day. And I'd been right in thinking that I could get out without difficulty when I wanted to. It would take only seconds to scramble up that sloping shaft.

My complacency was shattered by the sound of voices

above. I listened tensely. It could be ordinary passers-by—though that derelict piece of ground I'd stumbled over hadn't looked much of a thoroughfare. . . . The voices grew louder. I caught the crunch of heavy boots. The footsteps stopped at the hole. I knew then that the view I'd taken of my prospects the night before had been too hopeful. The blue-caps had come back to the place where they'd lost me.

A voice said, "If he is down there, *tovarischi,* we'll have a job to find him."

"You're right," a second voice said. "I had an uncle who lived in these quarries for more than a year when the Germans were here. He belonged to a big group of partisans. Every night they used to come up and kill a Fritz or two and steal more weapons. . . . The Germans tried everything they knew to winkle them out, but they never managed it. They lost so many of the men they sent in that in the end they gave up. It was the one bit of Odessa they never captured. It's a real warren. . . ."

Another voice, more authoritative, said, "We'd better take a look, anyway. . . . Down you go, Yuri."

I gathered up my few belongings, rammed them into my pockets, and retreated along the section of tunnel I'd explored the night before. After the first fork, I stopped to listen again. The blue-caps were slithering down the chute. They'd got torches—big ones, judging by the glow. Suddenly there was a sharp exclamation from one of them. I heard him say, "Look—*valinki!*" I guessed he'd found an impression left by my feet in the debris, and I cursed myself for my lack of foresight. Now they knew I was in the tunnel. But I still waited. Would they start searching for me right away or would they report back for instructions? I didn't want to commit myself to the unknown labyrinth unless I had to.

The answer came at once—swift footfalls advancing in my direction and a powerful beam of light. I'd left it late. I turned and ran, holding my puny torch in front of me. The blue-cap must have heard me, for his steps quickened. He was almost on my heels. For a moment his torch held me in its beam; and he shouted. I feared a shot, and spurted for a bend in the tunnel. I raced at top speed through the chamber where I'd found the candles, and kept going, not bothering now about which forks I took. Little by little I began to gain. I ran for perhaps a couple of minutes. Then, quite suddenly, the noise behind me faded, the footfalls died away. The blue-cap had taken a different fork. In a few moments, the silence was total.

I stopped and leaned against the wall, breathing hard. I'd no idea where I was now—or what to do next. I doubted if I'd be able to find my way back to the shaft, except by sheer luck—and anyway the blue-caps were there. I'd do better, I thought, to go on, and hope to discover another way out. My torch battery was beginning to fail, but I still had the candles. I counted my matches. There were seven. I lit the longer of the two candles and set off again, slowly, shielding the flame with my hand. I took alternate forks, so that I wouldn't walk in a circle.

That quarry was a fantastic place. The tunnels were like the veins of a giant leaf, spreading out in all directions, apparently for miles. They seemed to run under the center of the city itself as well as the empty outskirts, for in places the roof had been strengthened with steel props and concrete as though to take the weight of buildings. Once I thought I heard the rumble of traffic above me. Repeatedly I had to stoop under pipes or climb over cables that crossed the tunnel from side to side. I kept going, hoping all the time for an opening, but the passage continued without a break.

Hot wax suddenly burned my fingers, and my candle guttered out before I could transfer the flame. I groped for the second candle, a mere stump. It might last fifteen minutes, but no longer. My situation was growing desperate. Soon I'd be walking blind. The maze itself had become more dangerous than the blue-caps. . . . I lit the candle-end and set off again. I walked for five or ten minutes without finding any trace of an exit. Then a puff of air caught the candle flame and it went out.

I stood still in the darkness, wondering where the puff had come from. I couldn't see a thing, but I could feel a slight draft against my face. Then, as my eyes adjusted themselves, I became aware of a faint light ahead. A pale, natural light. I went quickly toward it. To my infinite relief, I found that it came from another shaft, very similar to the first. Twenty yards on there were two more shafts, close together—and beyond them, yet another glimmer of light. Outside the city there were evidently a lot of exits. They were all narrow, all with their heaps of earth at the bottom, all of the same depth. I imagined the partisans had made them. Or the Germans.

I stopped at the bottom of one of the shafts, trying to decide the best thing to do. My situation had changed dramatically in the past hour—and wholly for the worse. Now that the blue-caps knew I was down here they'd be certain to search every inch of the place. It would take scores of them, perhaps hundreds—but they'd have plenty of men and they could do it without danger. I was no partisan. Probably they knew where the holes were, too—they could station a man at each one, and prevent me leaving. Maybe they were already doing just that. The way things were, I was in greater danger staying in the quarry than walking in the city. I'd better get out—and fast.

I climbed the shaft and cautiously raised my head above the surface. The first thing I saw was a goalpost. I was at the edge of a sports field, with what looked like a factory at the far end. There was no one about, and I scrambled out. That was one hazard behind me, anyway—the moment of emergence. At once, though, a new one faced me. There was no snow. I hadn't realized it during my headlong flight the night before—but the ground was completely bare. And here was I, wearing huge felt *valinki* specially designed for snow! I wondered how many other people in Odessa were wearing them. There must be some, because I'd traveled with them. But it wasn't a good start.

I plodded along the edge of the field till I came to a gate, and went through into a rutted road. I was on the outskirts of the town. To the left, the country looked open. To the right, it was built up. I turned right, shambling along with my head tucked down in my shoulders and my eyes on the ground, the way a lot of peasants walked. Presently I came to a made-up road with new blocks of flats on either side. There were quite a lot of people about now. Some of them had quilted clothes but none was wearing *valinki.* One or two gave me odd looks as I shuffled by. A man on a bicycle grinned. A militiaman, with a cigarette dangling from his lips, watched me as I passed. I felt the sweat running down my spine. It wouldn't be long, I thought, before someone asked me for my papers.

I trudged on. I was beginning to get into the town now. The buildings were older and lower. There were trolley buses and cars, and busy crowds to give some cover to my *valinki.* Then, at the corner of a square, I spotted two blue-caps bearing down on me. There was a reading stand close by, with a glass-covered frame displaying copies of the day's papers, and several people looking at them. I wedged myself in among them and pretended to be reading *Pravda.* I learned nothing from it, except that the date was December 25th. Personally I'd have preferred to spend Christmas Day in the workhouse. When I looked round, the blue-caps had gone, and I set off again.

At a junction of roads I came upon a lively market, selling everything from colored drinks to furniture. I stopped and gulped down a bottle of mineral water. At least I needn't be thirsty when I was caught. . . . Then I noticed a second-hand clothes stall—with shoes on it! I sidled up and turned over a few pairs, looking for the oldest that would fit me. The shawled woman in charge glanced at my feet. "You've come a long way, *dyadya,*" she said. I nodded. "From Poltava. . . . It's cold up there." I picked out an ancient black pair that looked right, and tried them on, not hurrying. They felt fine. The only trouble now was the gap between the bottom of Ivan's trousers and the top of my shoes. I pushed the trousers down as far as I could without actually shedding them. I'd probably get by—I looked like a scarecrow, anyway. I haggled over the price of the shoes for appearance' sake, paid with a crumpled note, took my change, and went off with the *valinki* under my arm. Beside another stall, I put them on the ground while I fingered some material. Then, making sure that no one was watching me, I walked away.

I was no longer a cynosure and could pass safely in a crowd—but that wouldn't help me for more than a few hours. Without credentials, I wouldn't be able to seek a bed that night—and once darkness fell and the streets emptied, some militiaman would be sure to ask for my documents. What I needed now, and urgently, was that ticket to Moscow.

A large cash payment seemed the only hope. Speculators sometimes hung around the big railway stations and the city ticket offices, offering tickets they'd queued for. Or I might bribe someone again. I'd been lucky once, with the old peasant. I'd need a lot more luck in a place where the authorities were already alerted and searching for me—but at the moment they were probably still concentrating on the tunnel. I still had a chance.

I inquired the way to the main railway station, which turned out to be at the southern edge of the town. I was advised to make for the State Bank and then go straight down Pushkin Street, which would bring me out at the Square of the October Revolution and the station building. I set off at a steady pace. The route was easy to follow, for the center of the town was laid out in symmetrical blocks with regular streets between them. The pavements were broad and smooth and walking in light shoes again was a relief. I quickly found Pushkinskaya, a fine, tree-lined thoroughfare, and in fifteen minutes I reached the square.

One glance at the station building told me it was no place for me. Blue-caps were at all the entrances, checking documents. I was too late. Even if I could get hold of a ticket, I wouldn't be able to use it.

I turned away, unutterably depressed and weary. At the sight of those blue-caps a terrible lassitude had suddenly come over me. I'd no idea what to do now—and I hardly cared. At that moment I was close to giving up. If they were watching the stations, they'd obviously be watching everything—the airfield, the port, the exit roads. I was trapped in the town and I'd never get out. What was the point of prolonging the struggle?

I drifted off, no longer interested in where I was going. After a while I came to a park—Shevchenko Park, the notice said. It was high and hilly, and dotted with ancient ruins. There was an observatory at the top, and a pavilion restaurant. I suddenly realized that I was extremely hungry—that I hadn't had a proper meal since Sasha had fed me. I climbed the hill to the restaurant. It was almost empty. I went in and sat down under the window. When the waitress came I ordered cutlets and fried potatoes and a bottle of beer, with *pirozhni* and coffee to follow. She looked doubtfully at me and said, "Can you pay for all that, *dyadya?*" Momentarily I'd forgotten what I looked like. I showed her a note, a small one but sufficient, and she nodded and went off to get the food.

There was a fine view from the window—over the harbor and out to sea. It was almost like an aerial view. I could see the layout of the quays and moles and breakwaters; I could see the tops of warehouses and oil cisterns, and of the elevators that in better days had stored grain for export and now no doubt were storing it on arrival; I could see the ships in port. There was a biggish one, with a flag that I thought was Canadian, moving out of its berth to make room for another coming in. So near—and yet so far. . . ! I watched it maneuver across the harbor, let go its anchor, and tie up by the stern to a buoy. I watched enviously as a boatload of its crew put off for the shore. Free men! Men who could leave again. . . . Then my cutlets came.

The food put fresh heart into me. By the time the coffee arrived, I no longer felt like giving up. Moscow might be unattainable—but I couldn't be sure I was trapped in the town till I'd tried every way to get out. There must be many minor, unwatched roads—and I still had feet. The weather was mild and gentle, the terrain not harsh like the steppe. If I had to, I could sleep in the open. It was worth a try. First, though, I must re-equip myself. There was food on sale at the counter, and I restuffed my pockets with sausage, chocolate, and mineral water. I also bought, for a few kopecks, a tourist's plan of Odessa.

On a bench outside the restaurant, I sat and studied it. Along the northeastern side of the town, the harbor and docks with their attendant railway lines appeared to stretch for the best part of two miles. That way there'd be congestion, industry, and vigilant police. To the south, starting from about where I was sitting, the coastal strip was quite different. The plan showed it as conserved woodland fronting the sea. There was a place called Lansheron a mile or so along, which a note on the back of the plan described as a bathing station. That sounded more my mark. By keeping to the beach, I might be able to outflank the police cordon.

I took a path that dropped steeply, and soon emerged on the coastal road. It was more built-up than the plan had indicated, mainly with sanatoria and workers' holiday homes, but after a few hundred yards the solid buildings petered out, giving way to beach huts along the shore. This, evidently, was one of Odessa's summer playgrounds. Today, it was deserted—too deserted for my peace of mind. If anyone saw me, what was I supposed to be doing there? I found the answer in the shape of a small sack, washed up by the sea. I opened it and started to fill it with bits of wood as I walked along. Now I made sense. I kept close to the shelter of the trees, not hurrying. Occasionally I stopped and gazed out to sea. The water was placid, with only the gentlest lap of wavelets at the sandy edge. I passed several small rowing boats, tied to trees with their bottoms up. A little farther on there was a wooden shack, with nautical equipment visible through the windows. I could see rope, life jackets, rowlocks, oars. . . .

Suddenly I stopped. Oars. . . ! I looked back, to where the little boats lay—and beyond, to the granite wall of the harbor. Above it, I could just see the funnel of the Canadian ship. . . . It was crazy, of course—absolutely crazy. But wasn't everything I was doing crazy? Had I really any other chance of breaking out of this prison. . . ? Looking at those oars, I had an overpowering urge to put everything to one single test. . . .

I sat down under a tree and thought about it. I thought about the Canadian crew going ashore, about the buoy the ship was tied to, about the tremendous muscular effort I'd have to make, about the moon and the weather, about harbor patrols, about breaking into the shack. I tried to take everything into account. By the time dusk approached, I'd made up my mind. The dangers were terrifying, but the prize outweighed them. I'd risk it. . . . Before it got quite dark I returned to the line of rowing dinghies and picked out the one I'd use.

Getting into the shack was easy. The door was padlocked, but I broke a window with a piece of driftwood and climbed in over the clutter of gear. I chose a pair of oars with rowlocks tied to them, gathered up some oily rags, and climbed out again. I walked back quickly to the rowing boat I'd chosen. It was old and neglected, but it was the best of the bunch. For a moment I stood listening. The coast was quite deserted. I dragged the boat down the beach, launched it, muffled the oars with the rags, and pulled away from the shore.

The sea was as calm as a lake, and rowing was easy. There was no tide under me to speak of, and there was only a breath of wind. The evening was dark—though not as dark as I'd hoped. I'd overlooked the glow from the city, which the sea reflected. I wondered what else I'd overlooked. The oars creaked a bit in the rowlocks in spite of the rags, but not more than I'd expected. More worrying was the water that poured into the boat through the dried-up planks. At first it rose alarmingly around my feet and I had to stop rowing and bail with the only bailer I'd got—Ivan's fur hat. But gradually the planks swelled and the leak became no more than a trickle and I was able to concentrate again on what lay ahead.

I had a clear picture of the harbor in my mind—thanks to the tourist plan and the view I'd had from the park—and I knew just where I was making for. There was a mole, nearly a mile long, shaped like a shallow S and protecting the harbor from the east. I'd have to keep well out to sea to clear the end of that. At its tip there was a tower with a flashing white light, which I could see when I turned round. I didn't know whether the tower was manned or not. If it was, I might be in trouble. If it wasn't, I'd have no difficulty in slipping round the end of the mole and into the harbor through a wide entrance between the mole and a long straight breakwater. The steamer was anchored not far inside. I was gambling on its still being there when I arrived—and I thought it would be. If its departure had been timed for the early evening, I doubted if the crew would have been allowed to go ashore. Anyway, all was well so far, for above the mole I could see its mast-head light.

I pulled steadily through the tranquil sea, trying to conserve my strength for the ordeal ahead. It was hot work, rowing, even after I'd taken off my padded jacket, but as I got farther from the land the breeze freshened a little and cooled me. I kept a sharp lookout all the time for the lights of vessels, but the only ones I saw were well out to sea. Inshore, all was quiet.

It took me nearly an hour to reach the end of the mole from the beach. I turned frequently as I approached it, anxiously examining the tower. It was much bigger than I'd thought—a full-sized lighthouse with a gallery, and almost certainly manned. The reflection of its flashing light brilliantly illuminated the water around it. If anyone came out on to the gallery now, I was almost bound to be spotted. I breathed a prayer, and rowed for the shadow of the wall. I expected a hail at any moment, but none came. When I was right under the tower, I laid the oars gently across the thwarts and paddled with my hands. The faint onshore breeze helped me along. Little by little I crept past the end of the mole and on into the harbor. In a few minutes I was out of danger.

The steamer was now in full view, its lights blazing. It was about a quarter of a mile away, and stern-on to me. I couldn't see much activity aboard, but I could see a launch, tied up at the bottom of the gangway on the port side, and several men with flat caps grouped at the rail. Authority, without a doubt. . . . Checking all arrivals, until the steamer sailed. . . . Well, I'd expected that. What I hadn't dared to hope for was that a radio on the launch would be playing music. The sound came resonantly over the water, drowning any sound from my oars. I knew the song—it was called "Suliko" and was about a man who couldn't find his sweetheart's grave. A jolly little theme. . . .

I steered well out until I was past the buoy. Then I approached it from the starboard quarter of the ship, which gave me cover. I was afraid that when I reached it I'd be in the launch's line of sight, but I wasn't—the bulge of the ship's stern was in the way. The buoy was a round, flat object, with an enormous iron hook in the center. A warp, almost as thick as my wrist, was looped over it. From the buoy, the rope swept up in a graceful curve to the stern of the ship, entering at deck level. There seemed to be no strain on it. I could only guess its length—perhaps eighty feet. After the first inspection I preferred not to look at it.

I made the dinghy fast, put my jacket on, and climbed out on to the buoy. For a moment I debated what to do about the boat. If I left it tied up, it would be found by whoever came to cast off the warp. That could be fatal. If I set it adrift, I'd be finally committed to my enterprise—there'd be no going back. And an empty boat floating round the harbor could be almost as dangerous as one tied up—if it were seen. But it might not be seen for some time. Letting it go seemed the lesser risk. I untied the painter, gave it a push, and watched it drift away. It was only then that I remembered Ivan's hat was in the bottom. Not that it mattered much now.

I turned to the warp. I was scared to death, but waiting wouldn't make my trapeze act any easier. I considered the best way to tackle it. Could I do it hand over hand, swinging? I gripped the rope in both hands and pushed myself clear of the buoy. My feet dipped into the water. I worked myself along till they were free—and went on. Slowly. A little at a time, I told myself—that was the way. . . . Take it easy. . . . I covered a couple of yards without difficulty. The rope was still almost horizontal. But as soon as it began to curve up I was in trouble. Every time I moved along, my weight came almost entirely on one arm. I'd never do it that way. . . .

I swung my legs up and gripped the warp between my feet. Now I had my back to the steamer. I moved my hands along behind me and drew up my feet. That was better. The weight was more evenly spread, the pull on my arms much less. And now I could shove myself up with my feet. As the curve steepened, they took more and more of the strain. I kept going, a few inches at a time. I didn't know how I was doing—all I could see was the sky. I struggled on. The angle grew sharper. The muscles of my arms felt as though they were coming apart. I wasn't in training for these acrobatics. Once the rope tightened with a jerk as a breeze caught the ship, and I lost my foot grip and almost fell. I began to doubt if I'd make it. Yet there couldn't be much farther to go. My position on the warp was almost vertical. I pushed with my feet—and my head touched something hard. . . .

I looked up, and back. I could see a rail a foot above my head. The sight of it gave me new strength. One supreme effort, and I'd be there. I wound my legs round the rope and gave a desperate heave—and I was straddled over it, facing the ship. The rest was easy. I reached for the rail, hauled myself up, reached for the next rail, got both feet on the bit of deck where the rope ran through, and climbed over. I'd made it!

I stood there, soaked with sweat and trembling from excitement and exertion. Now what? I couldn't risk showing myself yet—there were sure to be Russians aboard. The afterdeck was empty, but it might not stay that way. I needed a hiding place. I crossed to an iron ladder and climbed to the next deck. Lifeboats. . . . The classic hideout for any stowaway. . . . I took a closer look at one of them. It had a tarpaulin cover over it, with complicated lines that would take ages to untie. Well, I didn't have to get *inside* the boat. I climbed the davits and hauled myself up onto the cover. It had a sag in the middle, and when I lay down flat I was pretty sure I wouldn't be visible from the deck if anyone came by. Apart from the fact that I was lying in a pool of water, everything was fine. . . .

The next few hours were as tense as any I'd lived through. I knew nothing of the ship's timetable. She might be scheduled to lie at the buoy for a couple of days. She might be going back to the wharf to take on cargo. If she stayed around long, the chances were high that my rowing boat would be found and a search started before I'd got clear. I lay listening, trying to interpret the sounds of the ship and the harbor. I could hear the faint throb of an engine somewhere below. That seemed a good sign. I could hear voices—some of them Russian. Once I heard loud laughter and the clink of glasses. A farewell toast, perhaps. . . .

It seemed ages before anything happened. Then, startlingly close, the ship's siren blasted off. Activity began to build up on deck. I heard someone call out an order, in a heartening North American accent. A whistle blew. An engine roared on the other side of the ship. That must be the launch leaving. The ship's telegraph rang and I felt vibration. We were moving. But only for a moment. The whistle went again, in the ship's stern. I guessed the warp was being cast off at the buoy. There was a hiss of steam and a rumbling noise from the afterdeck as it was hauled in. The ship's telegraph rang again and there was more vibration. Another stop. A deeper rumbling. That was the anchor coming up. More whistles. Now the telegraph was clanging every few seconds. The ship was maneuvering. Then the throb below grew stronger. Cool air began to blow over my body. A flashing white light threw its glow over me. We were passing the end of the mole. We were sailing. . . !

I longed to show myself, but still I didn't dare. The Russians claimed twelve miles of territorial waters, and I'd no idea of our track. For all I knew there was a pilot aboard who'd be taken off later. We might be accompanied. We could easily be pursued. That drifting rowing boat still worried me. . . . But the ship steamed steadily on. Its telegraph was silent. Its engines seemed to be going full ahead. I peered cautiously over the side of the lifeboat. To starboard, at least, there was no other vessel in sight. It seemed safe to reconnoiter. I grasped the edge of the boat and heaved myself up. I was in a shocking state. My hair and beard were matted with salt, my eyes were sore, my padded clothes were sodden and covered with black slime from the buoy. Every joint in my body ached. I had to use the greatest care in climbing down from the davits. Back on the boat deck I took another quick look round at the sea. There were no lights anywhere except our own. Just a beautiful emptiness. . . . I descended to the afterdeck. Two sailors were working there under the lamps, swabbing down. I approached one of them. He looked up at the sound of my step—and his jaw dropped.

For a moment he just stared. Then he called to his mate. "Hi, Joe, look at this—we gotta Russki stowaway."

The other man stared at me too. "Jeeze!" he said, in an awestruck voice. "Ivan the Terrible!"

The captain of the vessel was a big, tough, weather-beaten man from the shores of the St. Lawrence. His name was Nelson—and to me he was a greater man than Horatio. Once I'd told him who I was and he'd looked at my passport and heard an outline of my story, he got straight down to a salvage operation. He gave me a stiff shot of bourbon, let me use his bath, lent me a razor, looked out a suit of his own shore clothes, and regaled me with turkey and Christmas pudding. He was magnificent.

Over dinner I gave him a full account of all that had happened to me. I told him about Korzhenko and the blizzard and the lights going out; about the pipeline, and my hike across the steppe; about Ivan and Sasha and the old peasant; about the catacombs and the rowing boat and my desperate scramble up the warp. It sounded quite a saga, even to myself. He listened with a kind of fascinated incredulity, hardly interrupting at all. The thing that interested him most, of course, was what I'd done to trigger it all off—and that I couldn't tell him, for I didn't know.

"Well," he said, as I finished, "you sure have had an adventure. Best yarn I ever heard—I wouldn't have missed it for all the tea in China. . . ." He sat back. "The thing is, what the heck are we going to do with you now?"

"Where are you making for?" I asked him.

"Halifax, Nova Scotia. We'll be there in about two weeks. . . . I guess you're anxious to get back to England."

"As soon as I can, yes."

He pondered. "I could put you ashore at Istanbul tomorrow evening. You could fly back from there."

"That would be fine," I said. "I'd be most grateful."

"Got any money? *Real* money?"

"Enough to cable the office. They'll take care of me."

He nodded. "That's okay, then. . . . Now I reckon you'd like an early night." He got up, and so did I. His eyes were still fixed on me, still a bit incredulous. And a bit speculative. "Those Russkis must have had a mighty strong reason for wanting to bump you off, Quainton. . . . You sure you've no idea what it was?"

"I haven't a clue," I said.

It was true—I *hadn't* a clue—and I was much too worn out to start thinking about it again that night. Next morning, things were different. Refreshed in body and alert in mind after a wonderful sleep, and no longer preoccupied by danger, I felt capable at last of logical reasoning. So I began all over again, with the old question. *What had I done?*

Clearly, the offense I'd committed had been no minor one. What the Russians had tried to do to me, an accredited correspondent whom they'd thoroughly approved of and a guest they'd always treated well, was such an extreme step, so wholly without precedent, that I could only conclude I'd unwittingly threatened them at some vitally sensitive spot. They'd never have tried to kill me if I hadn't been, in some way, a serious danger to them. A danger that couldn't be removed by any other means.

How had I been a danger to them?

I still felt the starting point had to be Raczinski. He was the only new factor. Apart from seeking information about Raczinski, I'd done nothing in Moscow to raise a ripple. Over that affair, I'd somehow touched a nerve. How. . . ?

I thought back over my Raczinski inquiries. I thought about everything I'd said and done, in detail. . . . I'd looked up the case in the Lenin Library—as anyone might have done. I'd asked Pavlov for help, and he'd been sympathetic. I'd talked to a witness he'd produced. I'd talked to another one he hadn't produced—but he hadn't seemed to mind too much. I'd visited Lvov on my own—but it wasn't a military area, a place of state secrets. It couldn't be that. I'd returned with the gravest doubts about Raczinski's past. Nothing there for the Russians to object to. I'd planned to go to England for a showdown. Pavlov had approved and had promised me a visa. He'd actually got me the visa. If it hadn't been for the trip, I'd be in England now—and the Russian charge might well have been substantiated. . . .

If it hadn't been for the trip. . . ! Suddenly, I found

myself wondering. It had been pretty remarkable, the way Pavlov had laid on that trip with such lightning speed, a matter of hours before my departure. And pressured me into going on it by saying the chance might not recur. It was almost as though he hadn't wanted me to leave. As though it was my impending return to England that had hurried on the trip—and the plan for an "accident" that was built into it. . . .

Could it be that for some reason the Russians hadn't *wanted* me to get the whole truth from Raczinski? That they didn't want him put on the stand, and the charge against him proved. . . .

It hardly seemed likely—not at first glance. . . . But then I began to remember things—things that appeared to support the idea. The way the Russians had failed to press their charge, after Raczinski's condemnation. The way they'd ignored requests for identifying evidence. The way their propaganda had suddenly dried up. And, more recently, the strange alacrity with which they'd produced a witness whose evidence had turned out to be vague and unconvincing. A witness they'd brought specially from Tula to see me—a witness whose prospective evidence they could well have checked up on in advance. . . . In the light of all that, it really did seem as though they'd been trying to backpedal on the case, to destroy what they'd built up. As though, having condemned Raczinski, they now wanted to protect him. . . .

It was at that moment that the germ of a new and frightful possibility crept into my mind.

I thought back to Raczinski's story—its weaknesses and its gaps. . . . The extraordinary way he'd managed to survive all those camps. The fact that he hadn't troubled to change his name, that he hadn't hesitated to say he'd been in Loda. The fact that he'd given Lvov as his invented birthplace—Lvov, that had been Russian since the war, and was therefore virtually closed to outside inquiries; Lvov, where records could so easily have been made to disappear. The fact that the Russians themselves had apparently taken not the slightest interest in Raczinski's origins. The fact that Lutkin, the authorized spokesman, had remembered so little, and Skaliga, the fuddled and unauthorized one, had remembered so much. The fact, above all, that not a single incident in Raczinski's long saga of endurance and survival was capable of confirmation by any independent source. Even to Marya, it had all been hearsay. He had emerged from the war-fog of Europe with a baby girl—and he'd taken her to England. That was the total sum of proven fact.

I thought about Raczinski as a man—about the feeling I'd had that with his quality and caliber he would never have stooped to the vile betrayal of his fellow prisoners. I thought about his health—his unexplained anxiety state. I thought about his career as a research chemist, that had started with such brilliant prospects and had ended insignificantly in the laboratory of a cosmetics firm. . . .

I still had no clear picture of the truth. What I had was a most appalling suspicion. . . .

We were through the Bosporus and abreast of Istanbul by eight that evening. I thanked Captain Nelson in the warmest terms for the hospitality and courtesy he'd shown me, pledged the return of his clothes from London, and was taken ashore in a launch for which he'd signaled. As I'd arrived from Russia in an unscheduled ship, without luggage or a Soviet exit visa, the Turkish immigration officials were understandably curious and I had to tell them more than I really wanted to. They were pretty disbelieving to start with, but I finally convinced them that I was neither a liar nor a lunatic and in the end they gave me a forty-eight-hour transit visa and let me in.

The stay in Istanbul wasn't exactly a rest cure. I thought it unlikely the Russians could be on my heels already, but it seemed wiser to take a few precautions. I kept a close lookout for any following car as I left the harbor by taxi, and in the city center I dismissed the driver, walked a few blocks at a rapid pace, mingled with a cinema crowd, and finally picked out a very modest hotel—where I passed a quiet night. First thing in the morning I telephoned the office from the hotel. Cole hadn't come in, and neither had the Foreign Editor, but I managed to get hold of his assistant, Chalmers. I told him I was on my way home, that I'd explain everything when I arrived, and that I had to have two hundred pounds that day if not sooner. He took it all quite calmly and promised that the money would be at the National Bank that afternoon. I checked out of the hotel immediately afterward and spent the morning wandering in the city. In the afternoon I collected the money, did some basic shopping, and bought a ticket for London on an overnight plane. I dined in an unfashionable restaurant and at midnight I took a taxi to the airport. No one showed any special interest in me, and an hour later I was airborne.

I could hardly wait now to get home. There was one simple, practical check I wanted to make before I faced Raczinski. If he really was making cosmetics at Welwyn, it could only mean that I was on the wrong track and that my suspicions were baseless. I hoped he was. If he wasn't—well, that would be that. I had no taste for the role I was playing or the drama I felt pretty sure lay ahead—but I was too deeply involved in the affair to stop now. However shattering the end might be, I had to see it through.

I reached London Airport around nine in the morning. The day was Saturday, the weather dark and murky. Something of the apprehension I'd felt in Istanbul came over me again as I left the tarmac. If the Russians were keeping watch for me anywhere, this seemed the likeliest place. But no stranger eyed me, no one followed me—and very soon I ceased to worry. I called in at the post office and sent off a telegram to Cole saying I'd be in touch with him later. That way I could postpone explanations till after the showdown. I breakfasted in the airport restaurant, and immediately afterwards I hired a self-drive car and drove myself round the North Circular Road to Welwyn.

I got there about eleven. I stopped in the town and asked a policeman the way to the laboratory of Floria Products. He thought for a moment, and then said it was on the Hertford road—a couple of miles along on the left-hand side. There was a board up—I couldn't miss it. . . .

I followed his directions and in a few minutes I was there. A big black-and-white signboard beside the gate said "Floria Products Ltd. Welwyn Research Unit." The laboratory was set back about fifty yards, at the end of a concrete drive. It stood on its own, in surroundings of thick woodland. The building was a one-story affair, very white and clean, with a lot of glass. There were lights on inside, because of the murk, and I could see several figures in white overalls, working. Raczinski wasn't one of them. There was no one on the gate to ask me my business, so I walked up the drive to the front door. The door had glass panels and opened into a small lobby. Beyond the lobby there was another glass-paneled door, leading to the laboratory. I couldn't see any sign of a porter. I went through the doors and stuck my head inside the lab. There was a scent like the one I'd noticed in Raczinski's hall. A man with a test tube in his hand glanced up at me—and quietly got on with his work.

I stood there for a moment, looking around. No one took any notice of me. The place was as casual and informal as a public library. I went out again, feeling more cheerful. So much for my suspicions. . . .

I walked round to the back of the building. There was a car park, with spaces for a couple of dozen cars, most of them vacant—and that was about all. A low wire fence marked the boundary of the Floria Products site. It had a gate in it, latched but not locked, and I went through. Beyond the gate there was a path that lost itself in dark and dripping woods. Though bare of leaves, the trees formed such a barrier that it was impossible to see anything through them. Or was it. . . ? For a second, I imagined I could see a light. . . .

I was startled by a step beside me and a man's voice saying, "Can I help you, sir?" I whipped round. The man was big and burly and wore a commissionaire-type uniform. A badge on the front of his cap said "Floria Products Ltd." I couldn't think where he'd sprung from.

"I've a friend who works here," I told him. "Dr. Stefan Raczinski. . . . He invited me to look over the place some time, and as I was passing I thought I'd call in and see if he was around. . . . But he doesn't appear to be."

The commissionaire gave me a very odd look, which I couldn't interpret. "No, he's not in today, sir. . . ." Gently but firmly he shepherded me back through the gate. "Would you care to leave your name?"

"Quainton," I said. "Lord Quainton. . . . Anyway, I'll be ringing him."

"Very good, sir. . . ."

I gave him an offhand nod and walked back to the car. He strolled slowly along behind me. As I got in, I saw that he was jotting something down. I wondered if it was the car number.

I drove back along the road for half a mile and stopped at a lay-by. There was a gap in the hedge and I went through it and plunged into the woods. The ground was wet and muddy and choked with brambles that tore at my legs—but walking through them was child's play after climbing a warp. I pressed on, working round in the general direction of the lab. I kept going for about a quarter of a mile. Then I came out into an open space. Beyond it, there was a wire fence. The fence was a strong mesh, about ten feet high, with several strands of barbed wire running along the top. It was flanked by a wide, cleared area, like a firebreak.

I crossed the clearing and went up to the fence. Suddenly, a dog barked. . . .

I peered through the wire. In the poor light, I could see nothing but trees. I walked slowly along the boundary, seeking a better angle of sight. The dog barked again. It sounded much closer now. I hoped it was inside the fence and not outside. A moment later a man emerged from the trees beyond the wire, leading a big Alsatian. He wore the same uniform as the man at the lab. He was very tough-looking, with a granite face.

"What are you supposed to be doing?" he demanded, coming close to the fence.

"Just taking a walk," I said. I'd had enough of blue-caps—even English ones.

He gave me an unpleasant look. "Well, you'd better take a walk back where you came from. All this is private property."

"Out here, too?"

"Yes, it all belongs to Floria Products. . . . Come on, get moving."

I got moving. I'd found out all I wanted to know—*more* than I wanted to know. Whatever was going on behind that high, well-guarded fence, I was pretty sure it had nothing to do with cosmetics.

So there I was, with the shocking, ugly truth. Not all of it yet, but enough. Taken in conjunction with what had gone before, the logic was irresistible. . . . Raczinski was a brilliant scientist. He'd appeared out of the chaos of postwar Europe with a background that no one could check on. He'd said he'd come from Poland, but that had been a lie. He'd worked his way up to a position of authority in a secret establishment. When I'd discovered things about him that might have started a new inquiry into his background, the Russians had tried to kill me. So what did it add up to? That for all these years, Raczinski had been working not for himself but for Russia. That Raczinski was a Soviet spy.

I wondered if Marya knew.

VI

At that point I wasn't at all sure that I ought to go on alone. If my conclusion was right, the stakes had become incalculable. Maybe this was the moment to hand over to the authorities. . . . But what would they think of my story—with its many gaps. . . ? And suppose I *wasn't* right? Moreover, I was very reluctant to set the dogs on Raczinski before he'd had a chance to speak. The only danger I could see was that he might take fright when he heard I was back—and clear off. I knew I hadn't the right to risk that. In the end I decided to drive straight to Hampstead without telephoning. By suddenly showing up on his doorstep when he thought I was in Moscow, I'd make the maximum impact—and there'd be no chance of his slipping away.

I was slowed on the way back by heavy traffic and my own gloomy preoccupation with the coming interview, and it was after five when I reached the flat. I'd have felt almost relieved to find no one at home, but Raczinski's car was at the curb and there was a light in the top window. I could see Marya's shadow on the curtain. I steeled myself for the encounter. I hated what I had to do, but things had gone too far for sentiment. I climbed the stairs, paused for a moment on the landing, and rang.

Marya answered the door. I braced myself for her shock reaction as our eyes met—but it didn't come. No exclamation escaped her. Her face showed neither surprise nor welcome. "Come in," she said, in a toneless voice. She looked pale and strained, with black smudges of tiredness round her eyes. The drama seemed to have started without me.

I went in, quite bewildered. "You were—expecting me?"

"Yes—some time."

I still didn't get it. "Perhaps you know why I'm here, then?"

"I think so."

"I have to talk to your father, Marya."

She shook her head. "My father's dead." she said.

She turned away, into the sitting room. I stood for a moment, stunned by the news. Then I followed her.

"What happened?" I asked.

"He took something. . . . Some poison."

Conventional sympathy was out of place and I didn't offer it. "When was this, Marya?"

"On Thursday."

"Were you here?"

"No, I was in Ireland, working. The police rang me, and I flew back yesterday."

"Who found him?"

"The police found him. . . . He wrote to them before he killed himself."

"Did he leave any message for you?"

"He left his life story. . . ." She went to a bureau and took out a foolscap envelope. "It concerns you, too. I'll leave you to read it. . . ." She went out, and I heard her bedroom door close.

The letter, in a firm, angular handwriting, covered many pages. It was dated "Thursday afternoon." It read:

> My dear Marya,
>
> The moment has come when I have to tell you the truth about myself, which I hoped always to keep from you.
>
> I am a Russian, not a Pole. I was not born in Lvov, as you believe, but in Leningrad—then called Petrograd. My father was an engineer, my mother was a school teacher. They were both ardent supporters of the Rev-

olution, and they both played an active part in it. I was brought up as a second-generation Bolshevik, a disciplined and indoctrinated Marxist enthusiast. I studied science at the University of Leningrad and became a research chemist. I was considered to be a young man of outstanding ability and promise. I married your mother, who was also a Leningrader, shortly before the outbreak of World War II. I loved her dearly.

When war came to Russia I was required to go to Moscow to work on propellants, leaving her behind. Then the Germans reached the gates of Moscow and every man was needed in the line. I fought for two weeks, and was shot in the knee. After I had convalesced I was sent to Sverdlovsk to continue my work. Early in 1942 I had word from Leningrad that you had been born. Then your mother was trapped in the dreadful siege of the city. For me, as for so many, it was a time of unspeakable agony. I had to work, and—worse—to *eat,* knowing that her daily ration of food was a single fragment of bread, so small that it would be lost in the palm of a hand. Presently I heard that she had died of starvation.

It was immediately after this that I was approached by Soviet Intelligence, with a proposition. I was told of a plan to infiltrate the West after victory with selected men of high scientific qualifications, whose task would be to reach positions of responsibility in their chosen countries and report back anything of interest. It was suggested that I should train to go to England or America. I had no urge toward espionage, but it was represented to me that I could perform no greater patriotic service. By learning the secrets of the capitalist enemy, I would be helping to make Russia so strong that no one would ever dare to invade her again. I already had a deep hatred of the West: of the Germans, for their monstrous aggression; of the Allies for having deliberately—as I then believed—left Russia to bleed alone. I was greatly influenced, too, by being told that, if I agreed, my baby daughter would be brought out of dying Leningrad across the ice-road of Lake Ladoga and flown to safety.

I had only one anxiety. The plan was that I should take you with me when the time came—and though I wanted to do so, this troubled me. I was concerned about your future—about the effect it would have on you if you were brought up in the West and later discovered that I was a Russian and a spy. But I was reassured on this point. My tour of duty, I was told, would not exceed seven years after victory, and then I could return. You would still be young enough to readjust as a Russian girl, and would suffer no serious harm. The pressure was great, and I allowed myself to be convinced.

I now underwent a long period of training and preparation. A complete cover story was invented for me. I was supplied with a Polish background. Lvov was chosen as my birthplace because the Russians intended to keep it after the war and would be able to block any inquiries. I went through an intensive course of learning the Polish language, Polish history, and Polish ways and customs. I lived for several years among Polish Communist expatriates. Then, with the advance of the Red army, I visited liberated camps to study the supposed background of my war years. One of the camps I went to was Loda. I also visited Lvov after it was captured and made myself familiar with the places that would feature in my story. Finally, at the appropriate moment, with a few forged documents in my pocket, I set out with you toward the West. Much that I have told you about the displaced persons' camp and how I got to England is true. But the stories of prison-camp hardships, of my life in Loda, of forest resistance with other Poles—these were all untrue.

I was screened when I entered England, but not in a very thorough way, because of the great pressure of work on the security officers at that time. The fact that I had you with me, a child of three, was a big help in gaining sympathy and establishing my good faith, as Soviet Intelligence had foreseen. So were the frayed, forged papers in my tattered wallet, which I said had been preserved by the neighbors who had supposedly cared for you in Lvov. There was the photograph of your mother, carefully remounted; there was a forged marriage certificate and, for me, a forged birth certificate. Because of these things, I had no trouble.

The early years in England were comparatively carefree ones. I had no fear that anyone would recognize and expose me, for no one in the West had ever set eyes on me until I had already become a refugee. The chance that some Polish student who had actually been at Lvov University in the prewar years might meet me and fail to remember me seemed a slight and manageable danger. My work in London was absorbing and important—but not secret. So far, therefore, I had nothing to report—and nothing to worry about. I maintained a single contact with Russia, through an agent who called himself Frank. He lived here in Hampstead, in a flat which has a window visible from my study. We both had red shades over our reading lamps. The arrangement was that if either of us wished to see the other, we would show an uncurtained red light between midnight and five past midnight, but not otherwise. Our short meetings took place on Hampstead Heath after dark—our longer ones at the top of Chanctonbury Ring. There we could talk in the certain knowledge that we were neither overlooked nor overheard. . . . But at first we met hardly at all.

Then, as the years went by, I began to grow anxious about you again. First in Lucy's care, and then at school, you were growing up to be an English girl. In the sixth year, I reminded my contact of the understanding I had been given about returning. I asked that it should be honored. He brought instructions from Moscow that I must stay on. I think this was the beginning of my disillusionment.

By now, much notice had been taken of my work, and

not only in academic circles. I had reached the point where I and my colleagues could foresee an early and responsible government post for me in some classified field. First, though, there would be another security check. It was certain to be severe, and I had some doubt of the result—a doubt which I passed on to my contact. My interrogators, I felt, were bound to be concerned that all my background history was locked up in a city now in Russian hands, and that there was no one in England who could vouch for it from personal knowledge. At the same time, there was much in my favor. I had an apparently unblemished record in England, going back over many years. Most of my friends were British, or anti-Soviet Poles. I had no close relatives in Poland through whom I might be blackmailed. I had been careful to show no interest in classified work—on the contrary, when the possibility of doing a classified job had first been mentioned to me I had made a point of appearing reluctant. Above all, there was a great shortage of top-flight men. . . . However, I was uncertain. There had been several much-publicized failures in security during the preceding months, and the authorities were alert.

It was when I appeared to be in line for one of the commanding heights in my field that someone in Soviet Intelligence had the idea of staging a trial and condemning me to a term of imprisonment as a camp criminal. I was told, not consulted, about this. The intention was to offer too little evidence to convince, but enough to show Soviet hostility to me and so strengthen my anti-Soviet image. The two witnesses, Lutkin and Skaliga—about whom, as about much else in this letter, you must ask Tim, for my time is running out—were security men who had known me well in Moscow during the period of my training. The trial was quickly held, and sentence passed. Having made their point, the Russians allowed the case to drop. The ruse seemed to work well. None of the people who knew me believed the charge, so no smear stuck to me. The private view of the British authorities was that the Russians had made the accusation because they had learned through an agent that I was likely to be of use to the West, and were trying to sabotage me. In any event, I got through the screening without difficulty, and shortly afterward I started work as assistant director in a secret laboratory at Welwyn, which is in fact a government establishment. I had taken the big hurdle, and there was now almost no limit to the position I might achieve.

At this point I began to do the job for which I had been trained. I exercised great care in choosing my material, for I was afraid that a slip-up in Moscow might reveal the existence of a leak. But I passed some highly important information. At first I hardly questioned the rightness of what I was doing. It seemed to be my duty. Then, as time went on, I became increasingly aware of inner conflict. Not only was I still worried about you, Marya, but I was becoming ideologically unsure. New, and until now unadmitted, attachments to England had developed. I was coming to realize that freedom—Western freedom—was more than an empty phrase. I was influenced, too, by the Poles with whom I mixed. I heard their war stories. I talked to men who had been imprisoned in Russia. I was appalled to learn that allegations which I had always believed to be fascist lies were incontrovertibly true. All these things served to undermine my sense of purpose.

There was another factor, too—a personal one. Over the years I had grown very fond of Lucy—as you realized. There was nothing I would have liked better than to ask her to marry me, if I had felt free to do so. But I knew I could not bring yet another innocent person into my life of duplicity, and I had to remain silent.

The time came, and fairly soon, when my health began to suffer under the constant strain. I thought I might resolve my conflict by telling my contact I no longer felt physically capable of carrying on. It was naïve hope. His reply was that unless I continued to work loyally for Russia to the limit of my strength, they would find means—as they easily could—of denouncing me to the British authorities. I think I might have faced that for myself, for I felt morally bankrupt and desperate for peace of mind. A long term of imprisonment would have seemed like a release. What I could not face was involving you. I felt I no longer had any choice. I said that I was as anxious as ever to serve Russia loyally, that it was only my health I was concerned about, and that I would continue to do my best.

Then Tim came into your life—and into mine. I liked him, and I was happy for you. I hoped he would soon take you away, out of my tainted world. I wished only that he had not had the association with Moscow. My concern on that score sharply increased when he found out about the Russian court sentence on me, for I foresaw his natural reaction—his desire to get to the bottom of the affair—and your own probable response. And things turned out as I'd feared. I still hoped that in time you would come to some understanding with him, and I did all I could to influence you—but at first with no success.

When Tim went back to Moscow, I tried to help in a different way. I told my contact of Tim's interest in the case and of the likelihood that he would try to probe more deeply—which could be dangerous. I said that the breakup of the relationship between him and my daughter, as a result of his discovery, was causing me deep anxiety and upsetting my work. I urged that if possible the Soviet authorities should reassure him about the trial by producing witnesses so vague and unconvincing that he would be certain a mistake in identity had been made. I pointed out that the trial had long ago served its purpose, and that no harm could now be done by backstepping a little. I suggested that the two witnesses who had known me, and had been briefed to give evidence against me at the trial, should be rebriefed to be uncertain and hesitant in Tim's presence. In the case of Lutkin, as I subsequently heard, this was done. The trouble came only when Tim found and interviewed Skaliga on his own. Skaliga, because of his chronic drunkenness, was considered no longer safe to produce, and had therefore *not* been rebriefed. His muddled account was a mixture of his first briefing and what he personally knew of me. He described my wound as he had seen it in Moscow, forgetting that it was supposed to have been incurred much later.

Tim's visit to Lvov—which would certainly have been prevented if it had been foreseen—uncovered the second mistake. My talking in detail about the garden opposite the Lvov house had been a grave error—a nervous attempt to fill out my Polish story with convincing fact. When Tim returned from Lvov, reported his findings, and said he was coming back to England to question me, the Russians knew that my days as an effective spy were numbered. Having told a lying story, I was not now in a position to change it. One thing would lead to another. In the end, there would be an inquiry—and I would be exposed. The Russians would lose not only my present services, but the far more important ones they hoped for as my responsibilities increased. There was only one way they could be certain of maintaining me in my key position—and that was to silence Tim. The Ukraine trip was hurriedly arranged.

I knew nothing of any of this at the time—nothing of the Skaliga interview, nothing of the Lvov visit or its consequences. Evidently I was to be presented with an accomplished fact. It was only this morning, when I went to a meeting called by my contact, that I learned what had happened. He told me of the "accident" that had gone wrong; that Tim had been traced to Odessa; and that from evidence found in the harbor he was believed to have made his escape in a Canadian ship. The situation, he said, must now be regarded as critical.

It seemed unlikely that Quainton would at once have taken the captain, or anyone else, fully into his confidence in view of the personal and involved nature of his discoveries, but nevertheless I should hold myself in instant readiness to leave for Russia. Meanwhile, Soviet agents were keeping track of the ship's movements. If, as seemed very possible, Quainton was set down at some Mediterranean port, there might well be insufficient time to organize his liquidation before he flew home. But as soon as he reached London airport there would be men available to deal with him, and because the stakes were so high no risk would be considered too great. There was an excellent chance that he would be silenced before he could speak, without anyone knowing the reason, and that I would be able to continue my work undisturbed. . . .

So that, Marya, is the situation that confronts me as I sit here at my desk. The assassins are waiting for Tim. In the past hour, I have had to decide what to do. Writing this letter—this confession—to you has helped me to make up my mind. At first I considered surrendering to the authorities. Once I had given myself up, I thought, and the Russians had been informed that I had done so, they would no longer have any reason to kill Tim. I rejected that course because once again I could not face what it involved. The interrogation, the trial, the imprisonment, the denunciations, the obloquy of friends—yes. But I could not face the protracted humiliation for you—nor the thought of *seeing* you again, once you knew the truth. It seemed better that I should remove myself from the scene. This is what I intend to do. It will, I know, be a great shock to you—but in the end, for you as well as for me, it will be merciful.

I shall write some more letters now—one to the local police, enclosing the key of the flat, one to my contact, one to the Soviet Embassy. This will ensure that my body will be found in the morning, and that the Russians will know I am dead. I am confident that Tim will then have nothing to fear. Soviet Intelligence is too realistic to revenge itself upon a corpse.

That is all, my dear. I will not attempt to excuse myself. I am deeply sorry that I have brought so much trouble upon you. What you do now, I cannot hope to influence. You will have to decide—you and Tim. I have left you, I know, a dreadful legacy—yet I would have done anything for your happiness. Good-bye, Marya. . . .

The signature, for a reason I could only guess at, was spelt not in the Polish way, but as though it had been transliterated from the Russian. It was written "Stefan Rashinsky."

Moved and shaken, I put the letter down. So there it was—the whole truth about Marya's father. The facts I had known, and the facts I had not known. All in their place at last. The charge and the trial, the strange behavior of the witnesses, the readiness of Pavlov to help me—all explained. A fascinating story—fascinating, terrible—and tragic. . . .

My thoughts were in a whirl—but one thought stood out sharp and clear. *Marya had known nothing.* . . .

I called from the door, and presently she came in. Her face was without expression, a mask concealing everything but weariness. I wished she'd talk, break down, curse—anything. Anything rather than maintain that frozen front. I'd have tried to comfort her, but I knew she didn't want comfort from me. Whatever her father had done, the fact remained that I had been the instrument of his death. The gulf that stretched between us was impassable.

I concentrated on practical things. "This letter, Marya—it mentions a lot of things that you don't know about. Would you like me to explain them?"

"No," she said. "Not now. . . . I don't want to hear anything more."

"Have the police seen the letter?"

"No. . . . I didn't find it till last night—it was under my pillow. . . . I thought you should see it first."

"It ought to go to someone now," I said. "Someone pretty high up. . . . Shall I take care of that?"

"If you like."

"What's happening about the inquest?"

"The police said they thought it would be on Tuesday. They said they'd let me know."

"Was there much in the papers? I haven't seen one today."

"There was a bit in the *Times*. Just about him being found dead."

I nodded. "What about yourself, Marya. . . ? You oughtn't to stay here on your own."

"I'll be all right."

"You've had a terrible shock—you need looking after. Couldn't you get Tina to come and keep you company for a few days? Or go and stay with her?"

"I'd sooner be alone."

"Has Tina been in touch with you?"

"Yes, of course—but I said I'd be better on my own. And I shall be. . . . Don't worry—I shan't throw myself out of the window."

"I wasn't thinking of that," I said. "But I *am* worried. . . . I wish to God there was something I could do. . . . Isn't there anything, Marya—anything at all?"

"Nothing at all," she said. "Please go now. . . ." She went into the hall and opened the front door and held it for me. She didn't actually say "And don't come back" —but that was the message I got.

For Marya's sake, I would gladly have destroyed Raczinski's letter—but of course I couldn't. The authorities had to know that he had passed secrets, if only to judge what had been lost. I doubted if by now they'd be able to lay hands on his contact, Frank—but they had to be given the chance. And the sooner they had the information, the better chance they'd have.

I drove quickly to my old hotel and checked in. There I wrote a covering note to go with the letter, sealed the envelope, and took it along to Scotland Yard. I identified myself to the top man with the help of my passport, told him that the contents of the envelope dealt with a vital security matter, and got an assurance that the letter would be taken at once to the right people. Back at the hotel I rang the office and left word that I'd be coming in on Monday morning. Then I staggered up to bed. What with the flight from Istanbul, the trip to Welwyn, and the grim climax at the flat, it had been quite a day.

Sunday was so frantically busy that I hadn't a moment for private thoughts. I'd left my address at the Yard, and at an early hour a car called at the hotel and I was escorted to a conference of security brass in Whitehall. There, I had to go over the whole Raczinski story in detail and answer endless questions. The atmosphere was pretty tense and it was clear there was a big flap on. The talks lasted, on and off, until the evening, and by the time they were over I was pumped dry.

After dinner, I rang Marya at the flat. I wanted to make sure she was all right; and, whatever her feelings about me, I wanted to keep the lines open between us if I could. There were some things I still had to say to her at a suitable moment, and I didn't intend to go out of her life without saying them. . . . But there was no reply. I thought of ringing Tina Howell and asking her if she had any news. The trouble was that once Tina knew I was back in England she'd obviously want to know why *I* wasn't looking after Marya—which I wasn't in a position to tell her. And what would be gained? Tina certainly needed no exhortations from me to keep a watchful eye on Marya if she was allowed to—which she probably wasn't being. Reluctantly, I decided not to ring.

First thing on the Monday morning I went into the

office and saw John Cole. It was a frustrating and unsatisfactory meeting for both of us, because I'd been instructed not to talk to anyone either about the Raczinski affair or about my escape from Russia until the whole thing had been fully investigated. All I could tell Cole was that I'd got involved in a security matter and that that was why I'd come home. I promised to give him a full account directly I got clearance, which was all I could do.

More frustration followed. I still couldn't get Marya on the phone and her office didn't know where she was. I suspected that the security people had got hold of her, and that turned out to be the case. She arrived for the inquest next day in an official-looking limousine, gave brief evidence that her father had been suffering from depression, and was whisked off again before I had a chance to approach her. She looked very strained, but I comforted myself with the thought that she was in safe hands for the moment. The court's verdict was the customary one—"suicide while the balance of the mind was disturbed." There was no fuss, and the whole thing was over in an hour. Someone had been busy fixing it.

I made yet another attempt to get Marya on the phone that evening—but again without success. She was out so much that I thought she'd probably been installed in some hotel where she couldn't be got at. Wherever she was, she was making it pretty clear that she still didn't want to see me.

By phoning around next day I managed to find out that Raczinski was to be cremated at Golders Green on Thursday morning, and when the time came I went along. A few of his friends and colleagues were there—and so, of course, was Marya. I saw, without surprise, that she hadn't asked Tina, or anyone else, to be with her. There was the briefest Church of England service—the absolute minimum—and the coffin slid away. It was an odd thought that if things had worked out a bit differently Raczinski might have rated a pomp-and-circumstance funeral procession through Red Square and a plaque under the Kremlin wall for his services. However, he wouldn't lack posthumous publicity. I wondered when the storm would break.

I followed Marya out after the ceremony. There was no car waiting for her—at last she'd been let off the hook. One or two people spoke to her, and drifted away. I approached her, and said "Hullo," and asked her where she was going. She gave an indifferent shrug. "To the flat, I suppose," she said.

"Let me run you home, Marya."

"It isn't necessary. . . ." She still sounded cold and distant—but she didn't rush away. She just stood there, lonely and uncertain. I knew I'd never have a better chance to thrash things out with her. I opened my car door and practically bundled her in. Then I drove her to Hampstead.

It was only a short distance and neither of us said anything significant on the way. But as soon as we reached the flat, I opened with both barrels.

"Look," I said, "I know you're angry with me, and if you've decided you can't bear the sight of me any more, I suppose there's not much I can do. . . . All the same, I'm going to say my piece. . . . It's true that in a sense I brought this on you—if I hadn't been so damned persistent, nothing would have come out. And your father would still be alive. You could say I killed him. . . . But once I'd started, I *had* to go on—one thing led to another. And I only started because I wanted to smooth things out between us. . . ."

Marya stirred uneasily. "I know that," she said.

"Well, doesn't that make any difference? Do you *have* to treat me like a murderer—like an untouchable?"

"You're quite wrong," she said. "I'm not angry with you—not a bit."

I stared at her. "Then what's got into you? You're like a block of ice."

"That's how I feel. . . . Numbed."

"Are you grieving so much for your father?"

"No—I'm not grieving. . . ."

"Then what is it? Marya, you're all tied up in knots. Why don't you unwind? Talk to me. Let yourself go."

"All right," she said, in a low voice, "I will. . . . I'll tell you just what I feel. . . . I was fond of my father. I was grateful to him for the sacrifices he'd made for me. I admired him. I respected him. I thought he was a fine, brave man, who'd had a hideous time in camps and pulled through by sheer guts. And all those years, he was a cheat—a squalid, lying cheat. Dishonest, disloyal, double-faced. Every hour of every day, he deceived me. I'll never forgive him."

So that was it!

"He turned my whole life into a fraud. He made me believe I was Polish when I was Russian. He made me believe in a background I'd never had. He made me as false as he was. I trusted him absolutely, I believed everything he said—and he lied and lied. . . . He's left me empty—a husk. . . ." Tears gathered in her eyes. "How could he *do* it. . . ? How could he look me in the face, and smile, and joke—knowing all the time what he was doing. . . ? It was vile."

"Yes," I said—and paused. "I do understand how you feel, Marya. It must have been an appalling shock when you learned the truth. . . . All the same, if a man's a spy I suppose he *has* to deceive the people closest to him. It's part of the job—part of the price he has to pay. We know your father didn't enjoy doing it."

"He didn't have to be a spy."

"No, he didn't—but he wanted to serve his country, and his beliefs. And that was the way he was asked to do it."

"Are you defending him?"

"I'm trying to be fair to him. He was a Russian, and a patriot. He was also a Communist. He felt he was virtually at war with the West—and he accepted a thankless, dangerous job to help win it. I don't think that makes him infamous. In my book, every man has the right to choose his cause and do the best he can for it. Even the duty. . . ."

"But a spy. . . !"

"All right—'spy' is a dirty word. But we all use spies, whatever we call them—and sometimes, rightly, we honor them. . . . The men and women who were parachuted into occupied Europe during the war were spies—but God knows they weren't contemptible."

"That's not the same thing. My father swore he'd be loyal to England. . . ."

"And they'd have sworn they'd be loyal to Germany if it would have helped their work. Do you think they never said 'Heil Hitler'. . . ?"

"But they were working for freedom."

"Your father was working for all sorts of fine ideals, too, when he started. . . . Peace, brotherhood, no more exploitation—all that stuff. Or so he thought. In fact he was working for a tyranny—a monstrous tyranny that would have enslaved the world by now if it had been allowed to. You know it, and I know it. In the end, he knew it himself. Okay—so he was wrong. He chose the wrong side. But that doesn't make him despicable. It just makes him pitiful."

Marya shook her head. "I can't be so detached—or so forgiving."

"You must be, for your own sake."

"Think of the harm he did."

"He paid for it, with all he had. His life was a torment—you can see it in every line of that letter. And he killed himself to protect me, when he could easily have sacrificed me. . . . I don't think you have to be ashamed of him."

"I am ashamed—bitterly ashamed. And everyone else will be. His friends—my friends. . . . I can't face them, Tim. I can't face anyone. I feel so—degraded."

"Look," I said, "if everyone felt degraded who had a parent they didn't approve of, half the world would be going about in sackcloth and ashes. Whatever your father did, he wasn't your responsibility. You don't have to do penance for him. . . . Marya, you've got to snap out of it. You've got to try and put it behind you."

"How can I put it behind me, when it's all going to come out. . . ? You know what it'll be like."

"Yes—it'll be savage. But we'll survive. . . ."

"We?"

"We'll get married. We'll face it together."

"Married—*now!* You must be out of your mind."

"Why shouldn't we? Give me one good reason."

"It's impossible. . . . Just because you're sorry for me. . . ."

I almost shouted at her. "I'm *not* bloody well sorry for you. If you want to know, I'm sorry for myself. I love you and I need you and I want to marry you. I've never stopped loving you, not for a second. I want you for my wife and I can't get you. . . ."

"Tim, it wouldn't work. Not after what's happened. . . ."

"That's what you said before. You let your damned pride get in the way, and everything got botched up. Now you're doing it again—and we'll both regret it. . . . Can't you stop thinking about the outside world and just think of us—the two of us, with one life each, loving each other. . . . Marya, I *know* we can come through this, and be happy. Why throw the chance away?"

I left her soon afterward, with nothing resolved. I hated to go, but she said she was tired and she looked so exhausted that I hadn't the heart to badger her any more. Not that there was much more to be said. I'd stressed all the things I could think of in mitigation of Raczinski's actions and I'd told her that whatever he'd done I didn't care. If that didn't heal her trauma, nothing would. Nothing, at least, that I could do.

I spent a treadmill of an evening, thinking about her. I couldn't get the picture of her out of my mind—sitting there in the flat, white and drawn, unbearably hurt, adamant in her proud isolation. . . . I'd been *too* fair to Raczinski. No one had the right to do what he'd done to Marya—not for any reason on earth. Nothing mattered more than a human relationship. What else *was* there. . . ?

I had a few drinks, and sank deeper into gloom. I went to bed and had a hellish night, worrying about her state of mind. She'd said she wouldn't throw herself from the window and I didn't think she would, but it wasn't the same as being certain. First thing in the morning I rang her from my room, to reassure myself and see if she'd had any change of feeling overnight. But her phone didn't answer. I had some coffee sent up, which was all I could take. Presently Miss Phelps telephoned and said the editor would like to see me, and I made an appointment for eleven. At ten I rang Marya's office. They said she'd just phoned them, and would be coming in late. That relieved my anxiety about her safety—but not my depression. If she'd had a change of heart she'd have got in touch with me by now. . . . It was hopeless. I couldn't go on like this. I wasn't going to get anywhere with her—ever. She'd just have to go her own way. Cole had said something about another foreign assignment. Perhaps that was what he wanted to see me about. It was a good idea. I'd take it. . . .

I bathed and dressed, and at ten-thirty I left to keep my appointment. As I crossed the hotel foyer, a page came over with a note on a tray. He said it had just been delivered. It was from Marya.

A last good-bye. . . ?

I tore feverishly at the envelope. There was a single sheet of paper in it, with a single line of writing. It said, "Give me time, darling. Please give me time."

I knew then that everything was going to be all right.

About the Author

Andrew Garve was born in England in 1908. For some years he was a reporter and foreign correspondent for the London *News Chronicle* and was in Russia for that paper from 1942 to 1945. Outside of his writing, his chief interests are traveling and sailing, and sea adventures feature in several of his books. His work has been translated into all the main languages and has appeared in some twenty countries. He was a founding member and first joint secretary of the Crime Writers' Association in England. He is a graduate in Economics of the University of London. A list of his works appears at the front of this book.